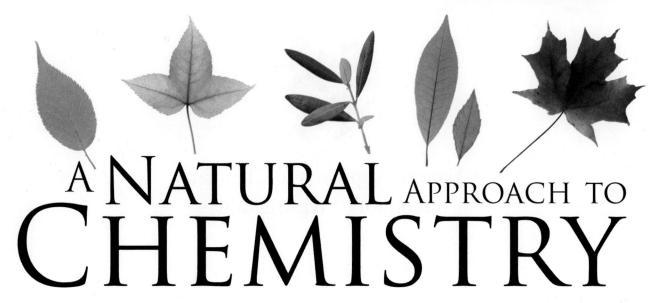

A NATURAL APPROACH TO CHEMISTRY

Laboratory Investigations

HSU
CHANIOTAKIS
CARLISLE
SHORT

LAB-AIDS®

A Natural Approach to Chemistry
Laboratory Investigations

Copyright © 2010 Lab-Aids, Inc.

ISBN-13: 978-1-60301-314-7

ISBN-10:   1-60301-314-8

4 5 6 7 8 9 10 RRD 15 14 13 12 11 10

Lab-Aids, Inc.

17 Colt Court
Ronkonkoma, NY 11779

This book was written, illustrated, published
and printed in the United States of America

About Our Investigations

We are strong believers that chemistry is best learned by actually doing it. We also know that many schools do not have specialized lab facilities for teaching chemistry to all students. Many schools are prohibited from using toxic or hard-to-dispose chemicals. Many schools may not allow use of open flames in their classroom. That's too bad because open flames are *interesting*! However, despite the legal and environmental restrictions we believe that chemistry can and should be taught in a hands-on, laboratory-based way. It just takes some rethinking about what experiments to do. It also requires designing some unique lab apparatus that makes hands-on, quantitative chemistry accessible to all students even without gas jets or fume hoods.

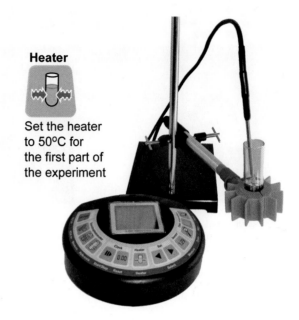

Heater

Set the heater to 50ºC for the first part of the experiment

We believe students learn more by investigation than they do in formal experiments. While we encourage you to have your students do a few formal lab reports, most of this book is just what the title says: investigations. There is no formal hypothesis because these sorts of investigations are what humans do when they are learning enough to *make* a sensible hypothesis.

This is what we have accomplished:

1. We have created labs that do real chemistry without toxic chemicals or chemicals that are considered hazardous waste. Virtually every experiment can literally be safely poured down the drain.
2. There are no open flames. Our Lab-Master unit includes a clever test tube heater that can boil 30 mL of water in 3 minutes and can be left on safely all night or longer. Even better, it gives you precise temperature control from room temperature up to about 150°C.
3. There are no fume hoods—all the experiments can be done in open air.
4. You don't need a specialized lab. Lab tables or benches are all you need (although a sink would help). We have taught the course successfully with nothing but tables, chairs, and electricity.
5. Quantitative accuracy to a few percent is obtained. Our stoichiometry labs really work!
6. We are not microscale. We don't believe students get excited when one drop changes color when it meets another drop. We designed experiments that are sensible and safe because they don't use very hazardous chemicals, not because they only use tiny quantities of hazardous chemicals.
7. We have designed a modern piece of lab equipment that includes an RGB spectrophotometer built right in. You can determine a pH with color indicators reliably and accurately.
8. A computer connection is available when you need it but not when you don't. Our Lab-Master automatically stores data in an open format on an SD card just like your digital camera. The data can be taken to a computer anytime, anywhere.

Tom Hsu
Manos Chaniotakis
Debbie Carlisle
Mike Short

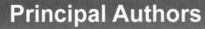

A NATURAL APPROACH TO CHEMISTRY

Principal Authors

Dr. Tom Hsu is nationally known as an innovator in integrated science curricula. He has developed a model for effectively integrating inquiry into science curricula. He is the author of six published middle and high school science programs in physics, physical science, and chemistry. Dr. Hsu did chemical engineering for Eastman Kodak, Xerox, and Dupont and also has taught grade 4 through graduate school. Dr. Hsu is cofounder of Ergopedia corporation. He holds a Ph.D. in applied plasma physics from MIT.

Dr. Manos Chaniotakis, a professor at MIT for 18 years, is recognized for teaching innovative, hands-on courses. He is cofounder of Ergopedia corporation, which develops inquiry-based science curricula, including books, equipment, and electronic media. He enjoys teaching high school science, which he does at every opportunity. Dr. Chaniotakis consults and develops instruments for the analytical chemistry industry, including meters for pH, conductivity, and ion concentration. Dr. Chaniotakis holds a Ph.D. in plasma physics and fusion engineering from MIT.

Debbie Carlisle taught high school chemistry, biochemistry, and biology for 20 years at Phillips Academy and other schools. She has worked with students at all levels of ability from introductory to AP. Debbie enhanced many important aspects of the laboratory program at Phillips that made it more exciting and accessible to students. Debbie has a master's degree in biological science, biochemistry, and technology.

Dr. Michael Short is a scientist at MIT. He teaches chemistry and general science for educational outreach programs at MIT. Mike has nearly completed his element collection and builds devices for molecular gastronomy. He consults for various companies on matters of material science, performing in-depth analysis and explaining real-world phenomona using fundamental scientific principles. Dr. Short holds a Ph.D. in nuclear engineering and a master's degree in materials science from MIT.

Consultant

Dr. Nikos A. Chaniotakis
Professor of Chemistry
University of Crete, Greece

Technical

Jared Sartee
Mechanical engineering

Adrian Culver
Laboratory experiments

Graphic Arts

James A. Travers
Lead graphic artist & illustrator

Reviewers

David M. Axelson
Chemistry Teacher
East Providence High School
Providence, RI

David Bain
Science Department Chair
Lakes Community High School
Lake Villa, IL

Kathleen M. Beebe
Chemistry Teacher
Portsmouth High School
Portsmouth, RI

Amy L. Biagioni, M.Ed.
Chemistry Teacher
Cranston High School West
Cranston, RI

Timothy J. Brown
Chemistry Teacher
Woonsocket High School
Woonsocket, RI

Jennifer P. Cameron
Chemistry Teacher
Lincoln High School
Lincoln, RI

Britany W. Coleman, M.A.
Chemistry Teacher
Lincoln High School
Lincoln, RI

Marina Dang, Ph.D.
Chemistry Teacher
Emmanuel College
Boston, MA

Ron DeFronzo
Science Education Specialist
East Bay Education Collaborative
Warren, RI

Reviewers

Janet Dickinson
Chemistry Lead Teacher
Kingwood High School
Kingwood, TX

Suzanne Doucette
Chemistry Teacher
Woonsocket High School
Woonsocket, RI

Brian Fortney, Ph.D.
Assistant Instructor
The University of Texas at Austin
Austin, TX

Judy Grubbs
K–12 Science Specialist
Region 7 Education Service Center
Kilgore, TX

Helaine Hager
Chemistry Teacher
E Cubed Academy
Lincoln, RI

Thomas J. Holstein, Jr., M.S.
Chemistry Teacher
Portsmouth High School
Portsmouth, RI

Pamela R. Kahn
Chemistry Teacher
Cranston High School West
Cranston, RI

Ronald Kahn
Science Education Specialist
East Bay Education Collaborative
Warren, RI

Janet R. Kasparian, M.S.
Biology and Chemistry Teacher
Portsmouth High School
Portsmouth, RI

Kimberly A. Laliberte, M.S., P.M.P.
Chemistry Teacher
East Providence High School
Providence, RI

Christine M. Lawrence
Special Education Teacher
Portsmouth High School
Portsmouth, RI

Deirdre D. London, M.Ed.
Chemistry Teacher
Cranston High School West
Cranston, RI

Donald Lurgio
Chemistry Teacher
East Providence High School
Providence, RI

Peter Madeiros
Chemistry Teacher
Woonsocket High School
Woonsocket, RI

Judy H. McGowan
Chemistry Teacher
Mount Pleasant High School
Providence, RI

Elaine Megyar, Ph.D.
Professor of Chemistry
Rhode Island College
Providence, RI

James Megyar, Ph.D.
Professor of Chemistry
Rhode Island College
Providence, RI

Janet M. Miele
Chemistry Teacher
Woonsocket High School
Woonsocket, RI

Roxanne Minix-Wilkins, M.S.
Science Program Coordinator
Region 5 Education Service Center
Silsbee, TX

Thomas S. Morra
Chemistry Teacher
Mount Pleasant High School
Providence, RI

Alana J. Nelson, M.A.
Chemistry Teacher
East Providence High School
Providence, RI

Dennis A. Nobrega, M.Ed. CAGS
Chemistry Teacher
East Providence High School
Providence, RI

Amanda Nycole Noble
Chemistry Teacher
Portsmouth High School
Portsmouth, RI

Leanne M. Gordon Perry, M.S.
Biology and Chemistry Teacher
Portsmouth High School
Portsmouth, RI

Kathleen Siok
Chemistry Specialist
East Bay Education Collaborative
Warren, RI

Jeffrey Soares
Science Education Specialist
East Bay Education Collaborative
Warren, RI

Kristian Fischer Trampus, M.Ed.
Director, East Texas STEM Center
University of Texas at Tyler
Tyler, TX

Keith D. Ward
Chemistry Teacher
Cranston High School West
Cranston, RI

Brenda G. Weiser, Ed.D.
Clinical Associate Professor Science
Education, University of Houston
Clear Lake, TX

Ellen Will
Chemistry Teacher
East Providence High School
Providence, RI

Donna M. Wise, M.Ed.
Science Specialist
Region 7 Education Service Center
Kilgore, TX

Judy York, M.S.
Education Specialist
Region 12 Education Service Center
Waco, TX

A NATURAL APPROACH TO CHEMISTRY

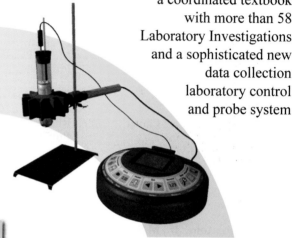

Program description

A Natural Approach to Chemistry is a system for learning including a coordinated textbook with more than 58 Laboratory Investigations and a sophisticated new data collection laboratory control and probe system

It all works together

Student text
Hard cover
21 chapters, full color

Student Lab manual
Soft cover
21 chapters, full color

Laboratory equipment package

Lab-Master system including

    Test tube heater (boils 30 mL in 3 min)
    RGB spectrophotometer
    Temperature probe
    Voltage probe
    Powerful and easy data collection system

Condenser with mounting ring
Desiccator
Foam insulation ring
Molecular modeling set
Ob-Scertainers
Atomic structure model sets
Element spectroscopy card set
Star spectroscopy card set
Dimensional analysis card set
Test tubes (25 mm)
Cuvettes
Cuvette and test tube rack
One hole rubber stoppers
Two hole rubber stoppers
Glass tubing
Inflation cap
Ring stand clamps
High-efficiency red LED
Alligator clips, 1 black and 1 red
LAB-AIDS audible conductivity indicator
Stainless steel electrodes
Electrochemical cell housing

Investigation 9B: Solutions and Beer's Law

Part 2: Collecting data

Clear instructions and experimental procedures

Place 3 mL of each solution into a clean cuvette. Add 3 mL of distilled water into a sixth clean cuvette. This will be used for your reference measurement. Start by performing the calibration using the reference cuvette. Next, insert a cuvette of each of the five solutions into the spectrophotometer. Measure and record the RGB absorption for each solution. This will provide the data that you will use to construct your calibration curve. Be sure that your cuvettes are clean. If your cuvettes are not dry, rinse them once with a little of the solution you are about to measure, discard the rinse solution and fill the cuvette with 3 mL of the appropriate solution.

RGB on
Activates the spectrophotometer

Reference
Calibrates the instrument with clear water

Measure
Makes an RGB absorption measurement

Color pictures illustrating the experimental procedures

Table 1. Absorption data

Solution	R	G	B
A			
B			
C			
D			
E			

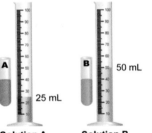

Insert cuvette

Part 3: Determining your concentrations

Guidance with data analysis

You may already realize that a serial dilution cuts your concentration by one half its original amount. Let's go through how you can determine your concentration.

1. For solution B (first dilution),
    the original molarity is $M_A = 1.0$ M, and the volume is $V_A = 25.0$ mL.
    We are solving for the new molarity (M_B).
    The final volume is $V_B = 50$ mL, so

$$M_B = 1.0\ M \times \left(\frac{25\ mL}{50\ mL}\right)$$

2. Use the same process for the rest of your test tube dilutions C, D, and E, and fill in the molarity column in Table 2. Transfer your absorption data into the R, G, and B columns of Table 2.

Solution A
M_1, V_1

Solution B
M_2, V_2

Quantitative relationships clearly given with units

Dilution formula

$$M_1 V_1 = M_2 V_2 \;\rightarrow\; M_2 = M_1 \left(\frac{V_1}{V_2}\right)$$

$$M_B = M_A \left(\frac{25\ mL}{50\ mL}\right)$$

$$M_B = 0.5\ M$$

Organized tables for data collection

Table 2. Concentration and absorption data

Solution	Molarity of CuSO₄	Absorbance Units (AU)		
		R	G	B
A				
B				
C				
D				
E				

A NATURAL APPROACH TO CHEMISTRY

A NATURAL APPROACH TO CHEMISTRY

Organization of the laboratory investigations

Chemistry is important, relevant, and learnable by all students.

Themes

Energy is a unifying theme that explains why chemistry occurs.
The atomic model of matter is consistently woven through every chapter.
Understanding of "why" chemistry occurs is emphasized.
Principles are illustrated with examples from the human body and the environment.

Chapters 1–4: Fundamentals

Present a comprehensive overview of all the main ideas in chemistry such as the atomic nature of matter, systems, temperature, and energy. Students don't get bogged down in the details, but see the conceptual "big picture."

Chapter 1	The Science of Chemistry
Chapter 2	Matter and Atoms
Chapter 3	Temperature, Energy, and Heat
Chapter 4	Physical and Chemical Change

Chapters 5–14: Core Concepts

Present in-depth coverage of all major topic areas. They develop *usable* understanding of the big ideas laid out in the first four chapters. The treatment includes strong conceptual development as well as algebra-based quantitative problem solving. *All academic content and instruction standards for chemistry have been met by the end of Chapter 14.*

Each chapter begins with a real-lab example as a point of engagement for the content of the chapter. One to three additional labs per chapter develop more aspects of chemistry.

Chapter 5	The Structure of the Atom
Chapter 6	Elements and the Periodic Table
Chapter 7	Bonding
Chapter 8	Compounds and Molecules
Chapter 9	Water and Solutions
Chapter 10	Chemical Reactions
Chapter 11	Stoichiometry
Chapter 12	Reaction Rates and Equilibrium
Chapter 13	Acids and Bases
Chapter 14	Gases

Chapters 15–21: Applications

Provide deeper exploration of significant areas of interest in chemistry. For example, Chapter 15 addresses the chemistry of rechargeable batteries. Chapter 16 addresses materials science, such as metal alloys. Chapter 21 looks at recent evidence for oceans of liquid water on Europa and Enceladus and the sulfuric atmosphere of Venus.

Chapter 15	Electrochemistry
Chapter 16	Solids and Liquids
Chapter 17	Organic Chemistry
Chapter 18	The Chemistry of Living Systems
Chapter 19	The Chemistry of the Earth
Chapter 20	Nuclear Chemistry and Radioactivity
Chapter 21	The Chemistry of the Solar System

Table of Contents

Chapter 16   Solids and Liquids

Chapter 17   Organic Chemistry

Chapter 18   The Chemistry of Living Systems

Chapter 19   The Chemistry of the Earth

Chapter 20   Nuclear Chemistry and Radioactivity

Chapter 21   The Chemistry of the Solar System

Appendix A

Appendix B

Appendix C

Appendix D

A Natural Approach to
Chemistry

Laboratory Safety

Doing chemistry is a much more interesting and engaging way to learn the subject than just listening to someone talk about chemistry, or even reading about chemistry. This book is about doing chemistry, and that means there are some rules that must be followed.

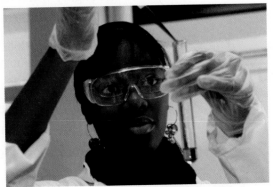

- Some chemicals are toxic.

- Some chemicals are irritating to the skin or eyes, such as bleach or acid.

- Some experiments will use heat sources that might cause burns.

*Doing chemistry is a lot more
interesting than just listening or
reading about it
but you have to be safe!*

For these reasons, it is important that you read, understand, *and follow* good laboratory safety procedures. Here is a set of safety rules to be followed during *all* laboratory activities *all* of the time.

1. Be responsible for your behavior. Broken glassware, spilled acid, and other hazards generally result from not paying attention or fooling around. There should be *no* running, pushing, practical jokes, or horseplay in a laboratory.

2. Wear approved eye protection at all times, except when explicitly excused from doing so by your instructor. You only have one pair of eyes, and they can be destroyed forever by a careless splash of acid. Don't let it happen to you!

3. Know the locations and methods of operation of all safety equipment, including the eye wash station, the fire extinguisher, and the safety shower.

4. If a chemical gets in your eyes, wash them immediately with flowing water from a sink or eye wash station for at least 15 minutes. However, *do not point a high-pressure stream of water in your eye*. Have someone alert the instructor and get medical attention immediately.

5. If a chemical spills on your body or clothing, alert your instructor immediately. Wash the affected area with running water. Remove any clothing affected by chemicals to prevent further reactions with skin.

6. *Do not* perform experiments that you have not been authorized to perform. This means using only the quantities your instructor provides. *Ask* if you don't understand the lab instructions.

7. Never remove chemicals from the lab.

8. In case of *fire*, let everyone know immediately and evacuate the laboratory. If the fire is small, you may engage a partner and use the fire extinguisher together to put the fire out. If the fire is larger, evacuate the building and pull the fire alarm.

9. If *you* are on fire, *get under the safety shower*. It is also your responsibility to assist a fellow classmate who is on fire to get under the safety shower.

10. Notify your instructor immediately in case of cuts, burns, or other injuries.

11. *Do not* eat or drink anything in the laboratory. You never know which chemicals may have been used on a bench or table. This rule applies both to food and to chemicals.

12. Wash hands thoroughly when leaving the laboratory. Many chemicals, especially organic solvents, can be easily absorbed through the skin.

13. Avoid breathing fumes of any kind. If you are instructed to smell something, use your hand to gently waft the scent near your nose. Do *not* stick your nose into the end of a test tube or into any chemical reaction container.

14. Although this course will not use such chemicals, a *fume hood* is necessary when working with many hazardous chemicals, such as strong acids.

15. *Never* use suction from your mouth to pipette a chemical. Use a pipette bulb.

16. Never point an open test tube containing a potential reaction at anyone. Outgassing, sputtering, and even flame can result from chemical reactions.

17. *Never* work alone in a laboratory. An instructor must always be present when you are in the laboratory.

18. Wear shoes in the laboratory at all times. Bare feet and sandals are prohibited. You don't want broken glass or acid on your feet!

19. Long hair and loose clothing must be tied back or restrained in the laboratory. Hair burns, and so do clothes!

20. Keep your work area *neat*. You are less likely to knock things over if glassware and equipment are not cluttered with books or papers.

21. Clean up spills or broken glass *immeadiately*. Use one of the bins provided for broken glass. No paper, plastic, or other trash should go in the broken-glass bin.

22. Know the fire hazards of chemicals you are working with. *Never* put flammable liquids near an open flame.

23. *Do not* force a stopper into a tube or a glass tube into a stopper. If you must put a tube through a stopper, use lubrication such as soap or glycerol and protect your hands with a glove or towel.

24. Be *alert* when handling glassware. A hot beaker looks just the same as a cold one, but it hurts a lot more when you touch it.

25. Read the entire lab investigation carefully before starting. You can get in quite a mess if you add chemicals in the wrong order, or if you do not follow the written procedure.

26. *Know* how to dispose of any chemicals or other waste you may generate in your laboratory activities. Waste containers are always provided for toxic or hazardous chemicals. There may be special containers or posters with useful disposal instructions.

27. *Always* replace the cap on chemicals when you have removed what you need.

28. *Do not* use dirty utensils to remove chemicals from their containers. Doing so might contaminate the entire supply.

29. Take only what you need, and *never* return excess chemicals to the container. This helps avoid waste and maintains the purity of the chemical supply for future students.

30. Clean up your areas before leaving the lab. Wash all glassware you have used and store it properly on a drying rack or other facility.

Safety Quiz

1. Before the first day of lab, it is very important that you know:
   a. Where the drinking water fountain is
   b. How to operate the vending machines
   c. The location and operation of the eye washer, safety shower, and fire extinguisher

2. There are some chemicals in the lab that are safe enough to taste. True / False

3. Some chemicals are irritating to the skin and/or the eyes. For this reason, protective gear must be worn when these chemicals are used. True / False

4. In case of fire or other emergency you should:
   a. Call you mom or dad
   b. Inform the instructor and leave the building
   c. Press the fire alarm and wait until the fire brigade arrives

5. If you spill a chemical on your hands you should:
   a. Use a paper towel to wipe it off quickly
   b. Rinse it off using an organic solvent such as ethanol
   c. Rinse it off using plenty of water from the faucet

6. When you have free time in the lab while waiting for an experiment to finish, you can:
   a. Chat with your friends
   b. Exercise your soccer techniques
   c. Review your notes for the next step in the experiment

7. What should be done if a chemical gets in someone's eye?
   a. Wipe it off with a towel
   b. Notify the instructor, then wipe it off with your hands
   c. Use the eyewash fountain, then notify the instructor

8. What should be done if a chemical gets spilled on your clothes?
   a. Remove the clothing that came in contact with the chemical (whatever that might be) and wash with water from the safety shower
   b. Wash with water to dilute the chemical
   c. Do nothing until you get home to change clothes

9. What type of footwear should be worn in the lab?
   a. Shoes are optional; you can go barefoot if you feel like it
   b. Hard-soled, covered shoes
   c. Sandals, which are more comfortable and cool

10. If you finish your experiment early, you can:
    a. Go to the next experiment to save time
    b. Spend your time talking with your friends
    c. Inform the instructor that you have finished, and ask for suggestions on what else you can do

11. During an experiment with glucose, a lot of clean starting material was left over, so you should:

    a. Take some home to use in your coffee or tea

    b. Take some to the cafeteria, so that you can use it they are out of sugar

    c. Never remove any chemicals from the lab

12. If smell is used to distinguish between chemical reactions in an experiment, you should:

    a. Place your nose close to the beaker so that the other smells around do not interfere

    b. Blow air into the tube so that the smell reaches your nose faster

    c. Wave the smell toward your nose slowly using your hand

13. At the end of the lab session, your experiment is running late. For this, you should:

    a. Stay in the lab to finish the experiment alone, especially if you know what you are doing

    b. Ask a friend to stay and keep you company

    c. Ask your instructor to stay with you; if he or she cannot stay, then you must go home

14. When a glass beaker or other glass container breaks, you should immediately:

    a. Pick the pieces up right away, so that the instructor does not take note of the accident

    b. Use your hands to pick up the glass, then use a mop or paper towel to collect any solution that was spilled

    c. Warn your labmates, inform the instructor, and use the proper tools to collect the broken glass. Never touch broken glass with your hands

15. After finishing with chemicals in the lab, you should:

    a. Pour them in the sink and flush with plenty of water

    b. Collect them in a large beaker so that you can dispose of them later all at once, so that you do not waste water

    c. Ask your instructor or read the label for the chemical you have used on how to properly dispose of the chemical waste

16. The best way to take the required amount of a chemical from the bottle is:

    a. Use a large spatula to take the required amount, and use the same spatula to return any unused or excess chemical back to the original container

    b. Pour the chemical out directly from the container, and return the excess back to the container

    c. Use a clean spatula to take the required amount, and dispose of any excess material properly

17. After finishing an investigation, you should:

    a. Leave all your glassware on the bench for the next group to clean up

    b. Collect the used glassware, place them in a container, and clean the work area

    c. Wash all the glassware, rinse with distilled water if available, and place them in the drying rack to dry

18. What should be the very last thing you do in the lab before you leave?

    a. Plan for the next experiment

    b. Make sure that your drawer is locked securely

    c. Wash your hands

19. At the end of an investigation, it is of the utmost importance to:

    a. Have good data to write your report, since you might not be able to repeat it

    b. Finish the experiment on time, and keep good notes so that any problems you have in your data can be accounted for

    c. All of the above, plus leave as healthy as you came into the class

A NATURAL APPROACH TO
CHEMISTRY

1A: Inquiry and Scientific Evidence

How can you discover something you cannot see or touch?

How do scientists know when they have the right explanation? Many of the fundamental ideas in chemistry have to do with atoms. Atoms are so small that you can't see them individually. This activity will show you how scientists "discover" what is unseen and also how to compare evidence to check whether your explanation is right or not.

Materials
- 3 Ob-Scertainer kits
- Pencils and paper

Part 1: Setting up

Ob-Scertainer

This investigation is about how scientists figure things out. Each of you will have several mysteries to solve. The mystery is the shape inside the black Ob-Scertainer. You have to predict what shape is inside without being able to look.

Hidden shape

Steel ball

1. Each group should have three Ob-Scertainer containers. Each has a small steel ball inside that can roll around inside a shape.
2. Open up the Ob-Scertainers and observe how the ball rolls around. Observe what kinds of sounds it makes. Take turns carefully rolling and tilting each one.
3. Close up your Ob-Scertainers with a steel ball in each one.

Part 2: Inquiry and scientific evidence

investigating an unkown shape

A scientific inquiry is an investigation to find the answer to a question. Your question is "What shape is in the box?" The inquiry includes all the things you do, and all the thinking you do to figure it out.

You will use a diagram to record your ideas about what the shape *might* be. This diagram is a hypothesis. A hypothesis is a tentative answer to the question.

You need to have evidence to support your hypothesis for what shape is inside the box. Scientific evidence must satisfy two very tough rules before being accepted.

1. **Rule #1: Objectivity**
    Being *objective* means stating only what actually happened, free from any opinions or suspicions. "The ball made five clicks on one complete revolution" is an objective statement. It says only what happened. "I think the shape is a star" is *not* objective because it is your opinion.

2. **Rule #2: Repeatability**
    When you or anyone else repeats the experiment the same way, the same thing happens, exactly as reported.

Part 3: Deducing the shape in the box

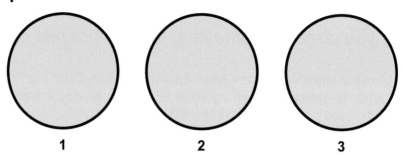

1
2
3

1. Swap your three Ob-Scertainers with three from another group. Don't open them.
2. Make and record at least three objective observations for each Ob-Scertainer that might help you determine the shape. For example, "I hear three clicks while rotating the Ob-Scertainer through one full turn." Your observations may include things that you did *not* observe, such as "I heard no clicks during a complete rotation."
3. Sketch a guess in the diagram above for what you think the shape of each Ob-Scertainer might be.

Part 4: Checking it out

Your groups should come up with a prediction for each of the three containers you have been given. Each prediction should be supported by at least one statement of evidence.

a.   Open the three Ob-scertainers.

b.   Sketch the true shapes beside the predicted ones.

c.   Was all of your evidence consistent with the actual shapes? Was any of your evidence contradictory?

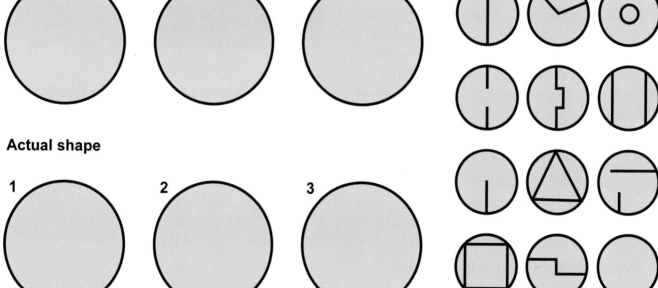

Guesses at the shape

1   2   3

The 12 possible shapes

Actual shape

1   2   3

1B: Volume and Chemistry

How are quantities of liquids used in chemistry?

Volume is an important quantity in chemistry. In many labs, you will measure volume in milliliters (mL). When we do experiments, it is important to be consistent in the way that we perform and record our measurements. This investigation will teach us how to work with volume measurement standards and techniques. These techniques will then be used for a number of other measurements.

> ### Materials
>
> - Four 25 mm test tubes
> - 100 mL graduated cylinder
> - 10 mL graduated cylinder
> - Test tube holders
> - Red, green, blue, and yellow food coloring
> - Chlorine bleach in a dropper bottle
> - Empty dropper bottle
> - Tap water

Part 1: Setting up

1. Measure 100 mL of water into a graduated cylinder

2. Add 1 drop of color to each test tube

3. Transfer 20 mL of water to each test tube

1. Measure 100 mL of water into a graduated cylinder.
2. Place one drop of food coloring in each test tube.
3. Add 20 mL of water to each test tube.

Part 2: Calibrating a dropper

Many experiments use very small volumes, such as one drop. In this part, you will calibrate a dropper bottle so you can measure one drop accurately. For readability, use water colored with food coloring to perform this calibration.

1. Read the volume in milliliters for 50, 100, and 150 drops.
2. Calculate the average number of drops per milliliter for each of the three volumes.
3. Calculate the average volume of one drop in milliliters.

TABLE 1. Dropper bottle calibration

# of drops	Volume (mL)	Avg. drops / mL	Avg. mL / drop
50			
100			
150			

Part 3: A chemical reaction

1. Measure 3 mL of one color into a small test tube.

2. Use the dropper to slowly add drops of chlorine bleach. Count the number of drops it takes until the color goes away and the solution is basically colorless. You may need to swirl the test tube a bit to mix the bleach uniformly.

3. Record the number of drops it took to become colorless.

4. Empty the test tube, rinse it out and repeat the experiment with another color. If you have time, do two trials for each color.

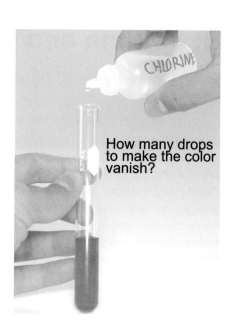

How many drops to make the color vanish?

TABLE 2. Drops to remove color from solution

Color	Drops of bleach

Part 4: Things to think about

a. What makes the color in food coloring?

b. Propose a possible explanation for why the bleach removed the color.

c. Did each color behave the same way? What does that suggest about the different colors?

d. Is the removal of color by bleach the result of a chemical change or a physical change? What evidence supports your claim?

e. Was mixing food coloring in water a chemical change or a physical change?

Part 5: A chemical mystery

One of the colors is a mixture of two others. See if you can determine which one is the mixture, and present experimental evidence that supports your claim.

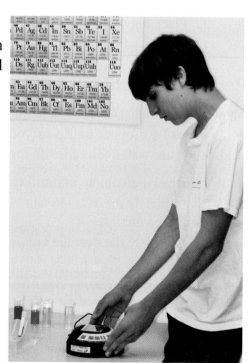

Part 6: Going further

a. Use the data from Table 1 and Table 2 to calculate how many milliliters of bleach it took per milliliter of colored water. This tells you the percent volume of bleach you need to remove each color.

b. Bleach is used in washing clothes because it chemically removes stains. Suppose your washing machine holds 15 gallons of water. How much bleach would you add to remove a yellow food color stain with the same concentration as your experiment? Use the following equivalents:

1 gallon = 3,785 mL and 1 cup = 237 mL

Name:_____ Section:_____ Date:_____

1C: Mass in Chemistry

How is matter measured in chemistry?

Chemistry is about learning what makes up the material world. Chemistry is also about how materials react when they are mixed, heated, or subjected to other conditions. Learning chemistry means learning to work with different substances, some of which are dangerous, in safe ways and in precise quantities. This lab will teach you some additional chemistry measuring and data collection skills.

Materials
• 4 covered vials
• 10 mL plastic pipettes
• Mass balance
• Liquid detergent
• Canola oil or similar vegetable oil
• Chlorine bleach in a dropper bottle
• Red food coloring
• Tap water

Part 1: Using the balance

Balance rules:

Use the balance on a flat, level surface.

Be GENTLE, place things carefully on the balance, never drop things.

Always use an appropriate container, NEVER put chemicals directly on the balance

Spills are to be avoided, but cleaned up immediately if they occur.

Zero button

In some chemistry experiments, we want to know what substances are present and precisely how much of each substance there is. In other experiments, we mix the right amounts of several substances to get something new. In both cases we need a method to measure things in a way that is both accurate and easy to communicate. Chemists use mass to measure and communicate quantities of matter. A balance lets us measure accurate amounts of mass.

Part 2: Measuring the mass of a liquid

Objective: Get exactly 10.0 g of water in the vial.

1. Put a vial on the balance. Place its cap on the balance too.
2. Record the mass in grams of the cap and vial.
3. Press the Zero (0) button on the balance.
4. Use the pipette to add and subtract water until you have exactly 10.0 g in the vial.

Part 3: Why use this procedure?

a. Can you describe another way to get 10.0 g of water in the vial?

b. What was the purpose of pushing the Zero (0) button on the balance?

c. Remove the vial with the water from the balance. Does the balance go back to zero? Can you explain why or why not?

Part 4: Adding mass

The next step is to add an additional 1.0 g of oil to the same vial.

1. Write a brief procedure that would allow you to accurately add 1.0 g of oil to the vial.
2. Add the oil following your procedure.

Part 5: The function of soap

You wash your clothes (and your hands) with soap. Soaps are a useful class of chemicals because of how they affect oil and water mixtures.

1. Add 10 drops of liquid detergent to the vial. Recap the vial.
2. By how much has the mass increased? (Record the mass of the liquid detergent.)
3. *Gently* shake the vial.

Part 6: Explaining what you see

a. Describe the behavior of the oil and water mixture before and after you added the detergent.

b. Propose an explanation for how detergent works.

c. Add 1 drop of red food color to the vial and mix gently.

d. Now let's add 10 drops of bleach to the vial. By how much has the mass increased?

e. Shake the vial and record your observations. What do you think happens?

Part 7: Doing the math

If you were designing a laundry detergent, you would want to tell people how much detergent to add to how much water. The percent concentration is a good way to give this information. The percent concentration tells you exactly what fraction of a mixture is soap, oil, or water. The formula for percent concentration is

Formula	Percent concentration
$\text{percent concentration} = \left[\dfrac{\text{mass of substance}}{\text{total mass}}\right] \times 100\%$	

Calculate the percent concentration of each of the three components. The total should add up to 100%.

TABLE 1. Percent concentration

Substance	Substance mass (g)	Total mass (g)	% concentration
water	10.0		
oil	1.0		
detergent			
bleach			

a. Is the concentration of detergent enough to disperse the oil in water? Why do you think so?

b. Should the detergent concentration be higher or lower compared to the concentration of oil?

1D: Dimensional Analysis

How do we translate between units?

Suppose someone said you were 3 m tall. How would you respond? Do you know how tall 3 m really is? You probably know that 3 ft is small for a grown human. So how may feet are equal to 3 m? This activity will help you solve conversion problems like this.

Materials
• Dimensional analysis cards
• Calculator

Part 1: How it works

1. Spread out your unit conversion cards so you can see their values.

2. You can arrange the cards to solve any conversion problem. For example,

Convert 2 hours to seconds

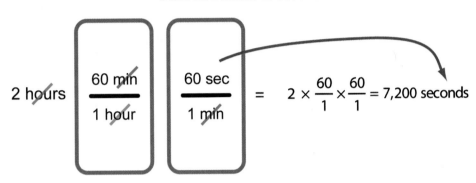

Part 2: Unit conversions to solve

a. How many milligrams are in 24 g?

b. How many centimeters are in 10 in?

c. Convert 45 inches to centimeters.

d. Which gas is more expensive: $3.95/gallon or $1.25/L?

e. Convert 23 miles to inches.

f. How many milliliters are in 1 gallon?

g. Which is longer: 100 m or 1 mile? Convert miles to meters to find out.

h. How many feet per second is 30 miles per hour?

i. Which is more: 1 L/s or 10 gallons/minute.

j. A construction project calls for 250 kg of cement. Your cement supplier sells 60 lb bags. How many bags do you need?

k. A doctor tells a patient to take 30 mL of a medicine. How many tablespoons of the medicine should the patient take? One tablespoon contains 15 mL.

Part 3: Area and volume conversions

When a conversion uses the same unit more than once, such as in area and volume, the conversion factor needs to be applied more than once. For example, a volume of 2 cubic meters really has units of m · m · m. This is denoted as m^3 (meter cubed). That means any length conversion needs to be applied three times. Here's an example: how many cubic centimeters are in one cubic inch?

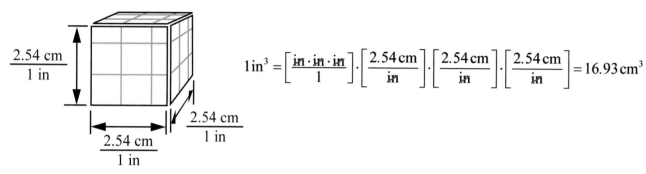

$$1\,in^3 = \left[\frac{in \cdot in \cdot in}{1}\right] \cdot \left[\frac{2.54\,cm}{in}\right] \cdot \left[\frac{2.54\,cm}{in}\right] \cdot \left[\frac{2.54\,cm}{in}\right] = 16.93\,cm^3$$

a. How many cubic centimeters are in 1 m^3? This is the same as the number of milliliters in 1 m^3.

b. How many milliliters are in 1 ft^3?

c. How many cubic inches are in 1 ft^3?

d. One liter is the volume of a cube that is 10 cm on each side. How many milliliters are in 1 L?

e. The displacement of a car engine is measured in cubic inches or in liters. The engine displacement is the volume of space that the pistons of the engine move in one complete rotating cycle. Which is a larger engine: one with a displacement of 4.3 L or one with a displacement of 250 in^3?

Part 4: Other conversions

a. An experiment is performed in a container that has a pressure of 25 psi. How many atmospheres is this pressure?

b. A submarine can withstand a maximum pressure of 20 atm. How many pascals is that?

c. A car is capable of producing 150 hp (horsepower). How many Watts does that correspond to?

d. An electrical generator can produce 1.5 hp. How many 100 W light bulbs can this generator supply?

2A: Mixtures

What does "pure" mean and how can it be tested?

Virtually none of the matter around you is "pure" because most ordinary matter is made of combinations of simpler substances. For example, pure orange juice is a combination of water, sugars, orange flavorings, dissolved salts, and other substances. To find what is truly "pure," chemists need to separate mixtures like orange juice into pure substances.

Materials
- Three vials with covers
- Three aluminum cups
- Granulated sugar, salt, and sand
- Conductivity tester
- Distilled water
- Mass balance

Part 1: Preparation

We will prepare three mixtures using three substances. Your task is to figure out what is in each one. The only clue is that the pure substances in each mixture can be sugar, salt or sand. You will need to use the properties of the three substances to determine which ingredients are in each mixture.

1. Weigh 1 g of each substance in each aluminum cup.

2. Put 35 g of water into each of the three vials.

3. Place the unknown substances into the vials, cap them, and shake them gently.

Part 2: Observations

a. Look closely at the three vials. What do you notice about the contents of the vials? Can you tell which is which by looking?

b. Let's start by figuring out which vial contains sand. Hint: Is sand soluble in water?

c. Now let's figure out which solution contains salt and which contains sugar. *(No tasting is allowed in the lab at any time.)*

d. Take the conductivity sensor and insert it into each solution. The sensor emits a sound when the solution is able to conduct electricity. Since electricity is conducted by ions, you should be able to deduce which solution has a lot of ions.

e. Look at your textbook for a clue as to which solution has ions.

f. Collect all your observations and list them in Table 1.

Insert the pins of the conductivity sensor in the solutions. Do you hear a sound?

Table 1. Properties of the substances in the three vials

Property	Salt	Sugar	Sand

Part 3: Composition

In real chemical detective work, it is usually not enough to know which substances are present. A scientist also wants to know *how much* of each substance is present. This is often quite hard to determine. The composition of a mixture gives the percentage of each pure substance that makes up the mixture. For example, 1020 steel has a composition of 99.3% iron, 0.2% carbon, and 0.5% manganese. This is an ordinary steel used in nails, garden tools, and cars, among other applications. Stainless steel uses less iron by having 10.5% chromium added to the recipe. Stainless steel is also strong, and has the added property of not rusting!

Steel is a mixture of different elements

1. Choose one of your mixtures to figure out its composition. (Hint: Some are easier than others.)

2. Write down at least one property that is different for the pure materials in the mixture.

3. Write down one or two sentences describing how you can use this property to determine how much of *one* ingredient there is in the mixture. Your procedure must give you *numbers* that allow you to assign a numerical value to *one* component of the mixture. For example, 33% sand is a numerical value.

Part 4: Doing the math

Here is an example calculation of the percent concentration of 10 g of sand and 20 g of water:

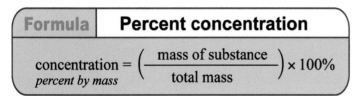

Formula	**Percent concentration**
$\text{concentration} = $ *percent by mass*	$\left(\dfrac{\text{mass of substance}}{\text{total mass}} \right) \times 100\%$

Example: Sand and sugar mixture

$$\frac{10 \, g \, sand}{30 \, g \, mixture} \times 100\% = 33\%$$

a. Use your data to calculate the percent concentration of each material that you used.

b. Calculate the percent composition of a solution made by mixing 2 g of salt and 15 g of water.

Part 5: Connections

a. Calculate the percent composition of sugar in a can of a (non diet) soft drink based on the information on the label.

b. If the density of granulated sugar is 0.85 g/cm^3, how many teaspoons of sugar are there in a can of soda?

A NATURAL APPROACH TO
CHEMISTRY

2B: The Chemical Formula

What is a chemical formula, and how is it used?

Paper, glass, plastic, metal, skin, leaves, etc. are all matter. Although different substances are made of different combinations of elements, there are only 92 elements on Earth from which all substances are made. In fact, only six elements make up almost everything around us. How does such incredible variety come from only a few elements? Compare elements to letters in the alphabet. How do so many words come from only 26 letters? The answer for matter is very similar, and the chemical formula is how we "spell" all the different kinds of matter with the same few elements.

Materials
- Molecular model kit
- Calculator
- Periodic table

Part 1: Setting up your model

Look at the molecular model kit. Assign colors to the different atoms, and write them down in the table on the right. Make sure you have at least the following four: carbon, oxygen, hydrogen, and nitrogen.

One color in particular should be assigned to a specific element. Which one and why?

		Element
	black	
	red	
	white	
	green	
	yellow	
	blue	
	purple	

Part 2: Making some models and "spelling" them

1. Pick any four atoms. Use the plastic bonds to connect them.
2. Draw the molecule you have made in the diagram below.
3. Use the yellow and blue boxes to work out the chemical formula for your molecule.
4. Write the completed formula on the line.

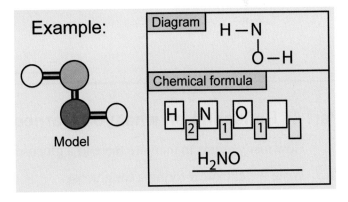

Example:

Model

Diagram
$H - N$
$O - H$

Chemical formula

$H_2 N_1 O_1$

H_2NO

Diagram		Chemical formula	☐ Write element symbols in yellow boxes
			☐ Write how many of that element are in your molecule in blue boxes

Part 3: Bigger molecules

1. Using six atoms, build a molecule with two pairs. A pair is two of the same atom.

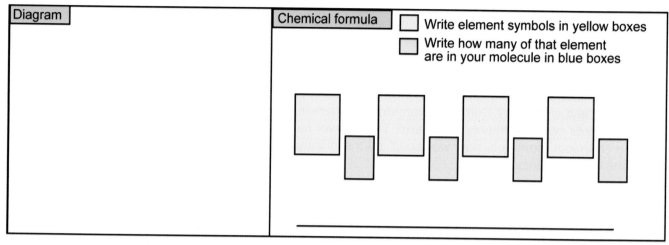

2. Using six atoms, build a molecule that has three of the same type of atom

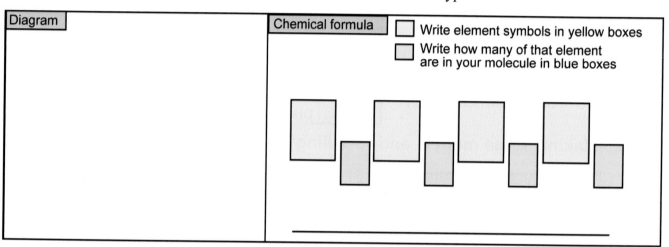

Part 4: Reflecting on what you learned

a. How many atoms in total are there in a glucose molecule?

b. Write the chemical formula for glucose.

c. Methane has the chemical formula CH_4. Draw a possible chemical diagram for a methane molecule. (Hint: Carbon makes four bonds with other atoms.)

d. Write a chemical formula for a molecule that has four hydrogen atoms, two carbon atoms, and two oxygen atoms.

Part 5: Rules for bonding atoms

In most situations, elements tend to form a specific number of bonds when they make molecules. For example, each carbon atom needs to make four bonds, a nitrogen atom needs to make three, and an oxygen atom needs to make two. This is one of the most important ways the elements are different from each other. They are different *because* they form different numbers of bonds with other elements.

12

Molecules can have single bonds, double bonds, and even triple bonds! Here are some examples of each.

A nitrogen molecule
has one triple bond

N_2

The oxygen atom in
a water molecule
makes two single bonds

H_2O

The carbon atoms in an
ethylene molecule make one
double bond between them

C_2H_4

Let's reassign the colors and set up the rules for bonding a few elements

	Element	Number of bonds
black	carbon	4
red	oxygen	2
white	hydrogen	1
green	chlorine	1
yellow	sulfur	2
blue	nitrogen	3
purple	sodium	1

1. Build one possible structure for each of the following molecules. Make sure you follow the rules for how many bonds connect each atom.

2. Draw a possible structural diagram for each molecule you build. There may be many possible structures for each molecule.

3. Leave the "formula mass" lines blank until the next step.

NH_3 **Formula mass** _____	Diagram
CO_2 **Formula mass** _____	Diagram

H_2S	Diagram
Formula mass	
CCl_2F_2	Diagram
Formula mass	
CH_3OH	Diagram
Formula mass	
C_6H_6	Diagram
Formula mass	
H_2CO_3	Diagram
Formula mass	
HCN	Diagram
Formula mass	

Part 6: The formula mass

The formula mass follows these rules:

1. Each atom has a unique mass.

2. The masses are different for atoms of different elements.

3. Each molecule must also have a mass that depends on both its chemical formula and the mass of its individual atoms.

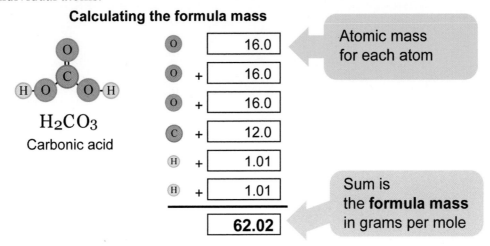

Calculating the formula mass

H_2CO_3
Carbonic acid

The chart is now expanded to include the average mass of each atom in atomic mass units (amu). An atomic mass unit is roughly equal to the mass of a single hydrogen atom. Carbon is about 12 times as heavy as hydrogen, oxygen is about 16 times as heavy, and so on.

		Element	Number of bonds	Avg. atomic mass (amu)
	black	carbon	4	12.0
	red	oxygen	2	16.0
	white	hydrogen	1	1.01
	green	chlorine	1	35.5
	yellow	sulfur	2	32.1
	blue	nitrogen	3	14.0
	purple	sodium	1	23.0

Use your diagrams and chemical formulas to calculate the mass of each of the molecules you built. Record the masses under the chemical formulas. You can use the diagram below as an example for one of them.

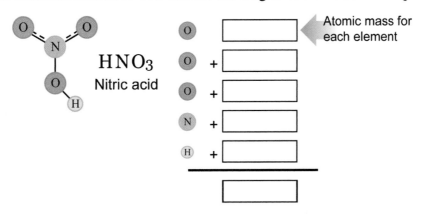

HNO_3
Nitric acid

2C: One in a Million

Drinking water can contain up to 1.3 parts per million (ppm) of copper and still be considered safe. What does parts per million mean?

Both living things and the environment can be greatly affected by small concentrations of certain substances. Sometimes the amounts are so small that we use parts per million (ppm) or parts per billion (ppb) to describe them. For example, fish live by extracting oxygen dissolved in water. Fresh water bass thrive when the concentration of dissolved oxygen is above 4 ppm. By releasing even very small amounts of hazardous substances, we affect the environment and sustainability. We can protect the environment by not releasing hazardous substances and by using various technologies to monitor environmental quality. In this activity, you will make solutions and measure concentrations in parts per million to understand the techniques and the skills used by scientists to monitor our environment.

Materials

- Five clean cuvettes
- Four 30 mL test tubes
- Cuvette rack
- Red food coloring
- Tap water
- 1 mL and 3 mL pipettes
- Lab-Master system

Part 1: Making solutions

1. Using the 1 mL pipette, add 1 mL of red food coloring to test tube #1.
2. Add 9 mL of water to the test tube.
3. Take 1 mL of solution from test tube #1 and put it in test tube #2. (If you use the same pipette, make sure to clean it well before reusing it.)
4. Add 9 mL of water to the test tube #2.
5. Take 1 mL of solution from test tube #2 and put it in test tube #3.
6. Add 9 mL of water to test tube #3.
7. Now take 1 mL of solution from test tube #3 and put it in test tube #4.
8. Add 9 mL of water to test tube #4.

Part 2: Doing the math

Each of the test tubes has a different concentration of red dye. In this step, you will calculate the concentration of dye in each one.

a.   First, calculate the concentration of the first. This is the solution that we made by mixing 1 mL of red food coloring with 9 mL of water.

b.   Next, calculate the concentration of dye in solutions #2, #3, and #4.

c.   Finally, calculate the concentration of each solution in parts per million (ppm).

Formula	Percent concentration
$\text{concentration} \atop \textit{percent by volume} = \left[\dfrac{\text{volume of substance}}{\text{total volume}} \right] \times 100\%$	

Example: Solution #1

$$\dfrac{1 \text{ mL of food color}}{10 \text{ mL of solution}} \times 100\% = 10\% \text{ concentration of red dye}$$

Dilution. Solution #2

Now we take solution #1 and dilute it 10 times to make solution #2

$$\dfrac{1 \text{ mL of solution \#1}}{10 \text{ mL of total solution}} \times 10\% \text{ concentration of dye} = 1\% \text{ concentration of red dye}$$

Dilution. Solution #3

Now we take solution #2 and dilute it 10 times to make solution #3

$$\dfrac{1 \text{ mL of solution \#2}}{10 \text{ mL of total solution}} \times 1\% \text{ concentration of dye} = 0.1\% \text{ concentration of red dye}$$

Now we take solution #3 and dilute it 10 times to make solution #4

Formula	Parts per million (ppm)
$\text{concentration in ppm} = (\text{concentration of red dye}) \times 1{,}000{,}000$ $\textit{parts per million} \atop \textit{volume}$	

In this formula, we use a decimal number for the concentration of the dye (for example, a 10% concentration of dye is written as 0.1).

If we were to use a percent concentration number, like 10 instead of 10%, we must replace 1,000,000 by 10,000. This can be confusing.

It is preferable to use a decimal number, since it is related directly to parts per million by the presence of the million in the equation.

TABLE 1. Concentration data

Solution #	Concentration of dye (%)	Concentration (ppm)
1	10	
2	1	
3	0.1	
4		

Part 3: Measuring concentration using the Lab-Master

RGB on

Activates the
spectrophotometer

Measure

Makes an RGB
absorption
measurement

Reference

Calibrates
the instrument
with clear water

Insert cuvette here

For many scientific experiments, the human eye is not reliable enough to make an objective measurement. For the next part of the experiment you will use the spectrophotometer in the Lab-Master to measure the absorption of the colored solutions.

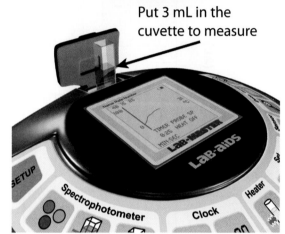

Put 3 mL in the
cuvette to measure

1. Put about 3 mL of clear tap water in a cuvette. Put the cuvette in the spectrophotometer. Activate the spectrophotometer and press **Reference**.

2. Put 3 mL of solution #1 in a cuvette, put it in the spectrophotometer, and press **Measure**.

3. Record spectrophotometer RGB absorbance readings along with the concentration data from Table 1 in Table 2.

TABLE 2: Spectrophotometer data

Cuvette #	Concentration (%)	Concentration (ppm)	Spectrophotometer absorbance		
			R	G	B
1					
2					
3					
4					

4. Repeat Steps 2 and 3 for solutions #2, #3, and #4.

Part 4: Observations

a. What can you say about the appearance of the four cuvettes? How do they compare to each other? Which is the lightest? Which is the darkest? Do any appear the same? Give two or three sentences.

b. Do your observations agree with what you expected?

Part 5: Thinking about what you observed

a. What does the spectrophotometer measure?

b. How low of a concentration of dye is visible to the eye? This is called the limit of detection by eye.

c. How low of a concentration of dye is detectable to the spectrophotometer? What is the limit of detection by this instrument?

Part 6: Plotting the data

Plot your data on the chart provided below. This chart scales the horizontal axis by powers of 10 so you can fit a wide range of values and still be able to see differences. On ordinary graph paper, a scale that would fit values between 100 and 100,000 would not be able to show the difference between 1,000 and 2,000.

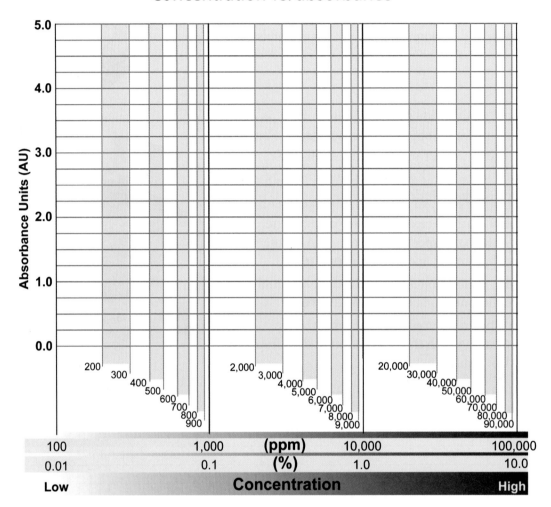

Concentration vs. absorbance

Part 7: Finding the concentration of an unknown solution

1. Get a sample of a solution with an unknown concentration from your instructor.
2. Measure the RGB absorption values for the unknown solution:

R = _____   G = _____   B = _____

3. Use the graph you created to determine the concentration of the unknown solution in ppm.

Part 8: Thinking about the experiment

a. What range of concentration can you measure with the technique you just used? Your answer should give both a lowest and a highest concentration that you think you could measure.

b. Do you think you could tell the difference between concentrations of 0.05% and 0.07%? Why or why not?

c. Can you tell the difference between concentrations of 0.055% and 0.057%?

A Natural Approach to
CHEMISTRY

2D: Density

Do equal sizes contain the same amount of matter?

Materials vary widely in their densities. A cubic centimeter of cork contains 0.12 g of matter, whereas a cubic centimeter of lead contains 11.34 g of matter, more than 100 times as much as the same size piece of cork.

Materials
• 50 pennies
• 20 nickels
• 100 mL graduated cylinder
• Mass balance

Part 1: The displacement method for measuring density

1. Collect 50 pennies and 20 nickels. Measure the mass of each collection of coins.
2. Fill a graduated cylinder to 50 mL with water.
3. Add the 50 pennies to the cylinder. Record the volume in Table 1 after the coins have been added.

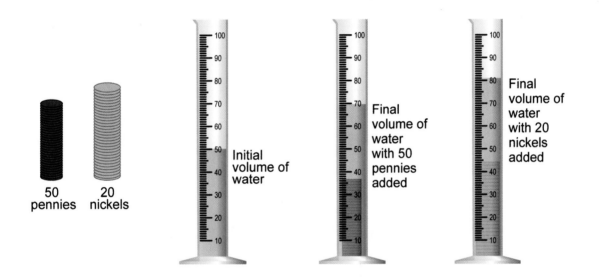

Table 1. Density data for nickels and pennies

	Dry mass (g)	Initial volume of graduated cylinder (mL)	Final volume of graduated cylinder (mL)	Volume of metal (mL)
Pennies				
Nickels				

4. Empty the graduated cylinder and repeat Steps 2–3 for the 20 nickels.
5. Calculate the volume of the coins by subtracting final and initial volumes.

Part 2: Calculating the density

Density describes how much mass is in a given volume of a material. The units of density are mass divided by volume, often grams per cubic centimeter (g/cm^3). Lead has a high density; it contains 11.34 grams of mass per cubic centimeter (11.34 g/cm^3). A one centimeter cube of cork contains only 0.12 grams of matter (0.12 g/cm^3).

Density

$$density = \frac{mass\ (g)}{volume\ (cm^3)}$$

$$d = \frac{m}{V}$$

- Density is a property of matter that is independent of size or shape.

- Density is mass per unit volume.

Table 1: Densities of some common metals

Metal	Density (g/cm^3)
Aluminum	2.6
Zinc	7.13
Iron	7.85
Nickel	8.80
Copper	8.93
Silver	10.49
Lead	11.34
Gold	19.32

a. Calculate the densities of the pennies and nickels.

b. Pennies have a copper color. Do your data support the conclusion that pennies are made of copper? Why or why not?

c. What is the most likely metal used to make pennies? (Use the data in Table 2.)

d. Which of the metals in the table might have been used to make the nickels in your experiment?

A NATURAL APPROACH TO
CHEMISTRY

3A: Heat and Temperature

What is heat? Are heat and temperature the same thing?

Temperature tells you whether something is hot or cold. You know that adding heat can raise the temperature. In this investigation, we will learn precisely how heat and temperature are related. Heat and temperature are *not* the same thing, but they *are* closely related.

Materials
• Lab-Master system with temperature probe
• Three 8 oz foam cups
• One 16 oz foam cup
• Hot and cold water

Part 1: Measuring temperature

1. Set up the Lab-Master system with the temperature probe.
2. Fill a foam cup about half full of ice cold water, *but be sure there is no solid ice in the cup.*
3. Fill a second foam cup half full of hot water.
4. Measure the temperature in each cup. Record these values in Table 1 along with the time of day to the minute.

Table 1. Water temperatures

Clock time	Cold water temperature (°C)	Hot water temperature (°C)

5. Let the cups stand while you answer the questions in Part 2. Measure the temperatures again after about 5 minutes.

Part 2: What happens?

a.   Consider that temperature describes a type of energy. Do you think hot or cold water has more of this kind of energy? Explain in one sentence why you think so.

b.   How do you expect the temperature of the water in each of the two cups to change over time?

c.   Describe the flow of energy that would cause the changes you predicted in Part 2b.

d.   Measure the temperatures in each cup and see whether the actual temperatures changed as you expected.

Part 3: Making heat flow

1.   Prepare a small foam cup with 100 g of hot water.

2.   Prepare a second small foam cup with 100 g of cold water.

3.   Measure the temperatures in each cup just before you mix them in Step 4.

4.   Mix the hot and cold water into the larger (empty) foam cup.

5.   Stir the mixture with the temperature probe and quickly record the temperature of the mixture.

Measure the temperature of the hot and cold water just before mixing

Mix the hot and the cold water and measure the final mixture temperature

Table 2. Temperature data for mixing equal masses of water

Cold water temperature before mixing (°C)	Hot water temperature before mixing (°C)	Mixture temperature (°C)

Part 4: Stop and think

a.   Which cup of water had more energy: the one with hot water or the one with cold water? Why?

b.   What did you think the temperature of the mixture would be? Why?

c.   If the system includes both cold and hot water, compare the energy of the system before mixing to the energy after mixing. You may ignore any energy going into the air or lost due to friction.

Part 5: Analyzing the data

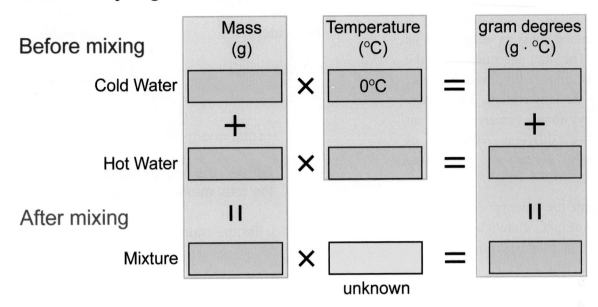

a.   Fill in the measurements for the hot and cold water, and calculate the gram-degrees of each.

b.   For the mixture, fill in the total mass and total gram-degrees. *Do not fill in the mixture temperatures!*

c.   What does the "unknown" box represent?

d.   Calculate the unknown temperature from the mass and total gram-degrees.

e.   How close did this value come to your actual measured temperature?

Part 6: A more complex experiment

1. Prepare three foam cups containing different amounts of hot and cold water. This time, measure the mass of water in each cup. Use at least 100 g of water of any temperature.

2. Measure and record the temperatures before mixing.

3. Mix the water in a large foam cup, stir well, and measure the final temperature.

What happens when you add three cups together at different temperatures?

Table 3. Data for mixing unequal masses of water

Sample	Mass (g)	Temperature (°C)
Cup #1		
Cup #2		
Cup #3		
Mixture		

Investigation 3A: Heat and Temperature

Part 7: Doing the math

The thermal energy associated with a certain amount of mass is related to its temperature. The thermal energy in the water is proportional to the mass of water multiplied by the temperature. The energy is only proportional because different materials store different amounts of thermal energy, even at the same temperature.

For now, assume the "energy" is in units of gram-degrees, or g·°C. Here's how to think about the experiment in terms of energy:

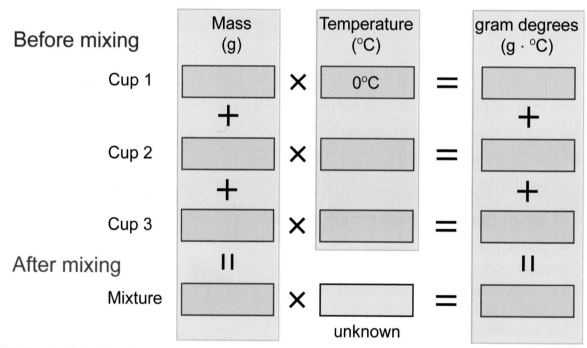

a. Fill in the light blue boxes in the "Before mixing" section. Calculate the gram-degrees for both hot and cold water.

b. Add up the masses and the gram-degrees to get the total mass and gram-degrees for the mixture.

c. Solve the "After mixing" section to get the mixture temperature.

Part 8: Why did the calculation work?

a. Did the result of the experiment agree with your prediction? Discuss the meaning of "agree" in terms of the accuracy and precision of your experiment.

b. Assume you have 10 cups of water with different masses and temperatures. Describe a way to predict the temperature of the mixture if you know the masses and temperatures of the water in the cups.

c. Describe a situation where two objects have the same temperature but different amounts of energy.

d. Describe a situation where two objects have the same energy but different temperatures.

26

3B: Specific Heat

If you know the temperature of something, how much energy does it have?

Two objects of the same mass and the same temperature can have different amounts of energy. This may seem odd, but it is true. Do the experiment and see for yourself.

Materials	
• Ten 1/2" steel washers tied with a string	• Mass balance
	• Lab-Master with temperature probe
• Ice	
• Water	• Two 8 oz foam cups

Part 1: The experiment

Tare the balance to 0.0 with an empty cup. Then measure the mass of at least 100 g of steel washers in the cup.

Cover the steel washers with crushed ice and a little water. Measure the cold water temperature.

Measure out 100 g of hot water in a second foam cup

Measure the hot water temperature just before mixing.

Remove the cold steel washers quickly and drop them in the hot water. Stir for a minute or so, then record the final temperature. *Be sure you do not get any ice in the water!*

Table 1. Temperature data for combining water and steel washers

Washer mass (g)	Washer temp. before mixing (°C)	Hot water mass (g)	Hot water temp. before mixing (°C)	Mixture temp. (°C)

Part 2: Analyzing the data

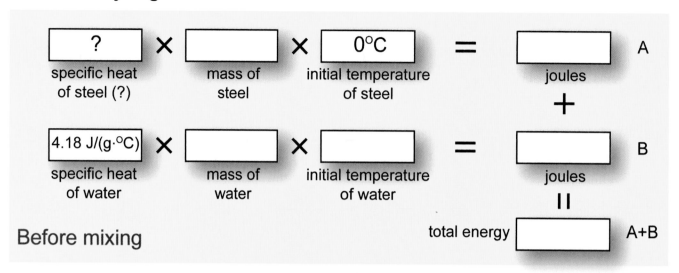

Before mixing

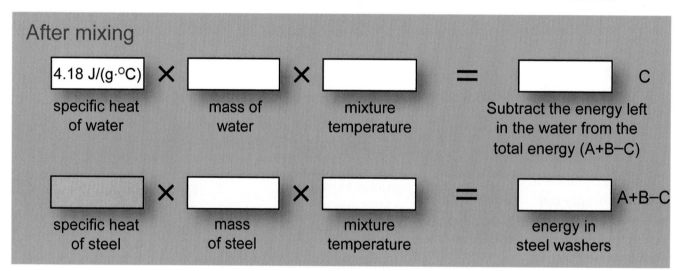

Part 3: Thinking about what you observed

a. Propose an explanation for why the temperature of the steel and water mixture did *not* come out halfway between the two original temperatures, even though you mixed equal masses of steel and water.

b. Now that you have a measurement of the specific heat, assume 0°C represents zero relative energy. (This means that we are measuring the energy relative to 0°C, not that the actual energy is zero.) How many joules of energy did the steel contribute to the mixture?

c. How many joules of energy did the water contribute to the mixture?

d. How good was the approximation we started with, that the steel contributed *no* energy to the mixture?

e. Go back and recalculate the total energy using the actual energy for the steel. Use the actual temperature you measured for the steel just before mixing.

f. Now calculate a new (more accurate) value for the specific heat of steel. How different is this new value from the one you had?

Part 4: The specific heat of steel

Specific heat is a property of a material that describes how temperature and thermal energy are related. For example, the specific heat of water is 4.18 J/g·°C. That means it takes 4.18 J of energy to raise the temperature of 1 g of water by 1°C.

The total amount of thermal energy stored in a material depends on three things:

- specific heat,
- mass, and
- temperature.

The relationship among these is:

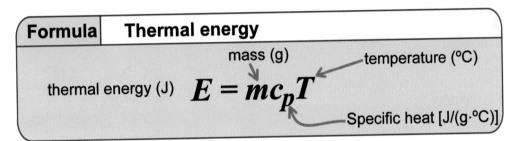

Example: How much energy is needed to raise the temperature of 10 g of water by 1°C?

$$E = (10\,g) \times (4.18\,J/g^{\circ}C) \times (1^{\circ}C)$$
$$= 41.8\,J$$

Part 5: Problems to think about

a. Suppose you add 100 J of energy to 50 g of water. By how much will the temperature of the water increase?

b. Describe a situation where two objects have the same mass and the same temperature but different amounts of thermal energy.

c. Describe a situation where two objects have the same mass and the same amount of thermal energy but different temperatures.

d. The specific heat of gold is 0.13 J/g·°C. Suppose you add 100 g of gold at 100°C to 100 g of water at 0°C. Is the mixture temperature likely to be

    i.   closer to 0°C than to 50°C,

    ii.   closer to 100°C than to 50°C, or

    iii. around 50°C?

e. Explain why the mixture will be at this temperature.

Part 6: Were we sloppy with our math?

We ignored the energy contained in the steel when it was cold. We assumed that the temperature was 0°C: therefore it did not matter what the specific heat was. With our old assumption, the contribution would still be zero. Of course, this is not exactly true! You likely found that the actual temperature of the steel was higher than zero.

a.   The diagram below is similar to the one used on page 28. Here we will enter the value of specific heat you calculated in Part 2. Here we will enter the actual temperature of the steel.

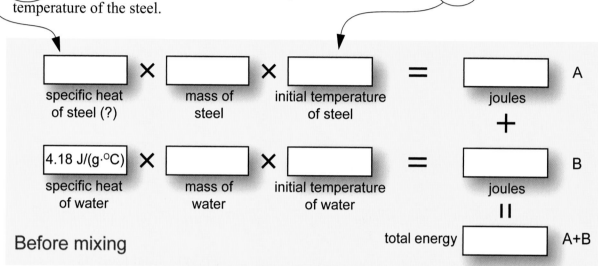

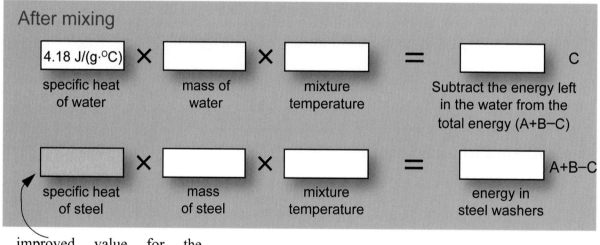

improved   value   for   the specific heat of steel

b.   Calculate the energy contribution from the steel.

c.   Is the energy from the steel large or small compared to the energy in the water?

d.   Complete the calculation using your value for the specific heat of steel. By the time you get to the bottom of the chart, your new answer will be a better estimate for the specific heat of steel.

e.   Is the new estimate close to the first one? Why do you think that is?

The technique you just learned is called <u>successive approximation</u>. At first we made an assumption that allowed us to get to an answer. We then used our answer to check our assumption and arrived at an even better answer.

A NATURAL APPROACH TO
CHEMISTRY

3C: Heat Flow and Thermal Equilibrium

Why and how does heat flow?

Everybody knows that an ice-cold drink warms up if you leave it in a warm room. The drink gets warmer, so heat energy must be flowing into it. When the drink gets to the same temperature as the room, however, it stops warming up. What slows down and eventually stops the flow of heat energy from the room to the drink?

Materials

- Lab-Master with temperature probe and heater
- One-hole rubber stopper with insulation ring
- Cold tap water
- 25 mm test tube

Part 1: Temperature and heat

a. Set up the Lab-Master with the heater and a temperature probe.

b. Fill the test tube with room-temperature water until the level is just above the lip of the test tube heater. The temperature probe should be below the surface of the water.

c. Set the heater to 50°C.

d. Record the temperature every 30 s for 5 minutes in the appropriate column of Table 1 (see p. 32). Make sure that you continually stir the water with the temperature probe while taking measurements.

e. Repeat Steps b–d, but with the heater temperature set to 100°C.

f. Plot the data from Table 1 on the graph paper below the table. Use a different color for each set of data. A good graph must have labeled axes, and each data point must be presented clearly. [Here for example you may label the horizontal axis "Time (s)" and the vertical axis "Water temperature (°C)."]

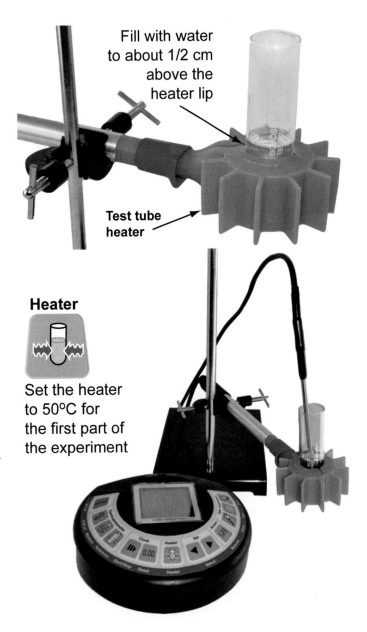

Fill with water to about 1/2 cm above the heater lip

Test tube heater

Heater

Set the heater to 50°C for the first part of the experiment

Table 1. Water temperature (°C)

Time (min)	Heater set to 50°C	Heater set to 100°C
0.0		
0.5		
1.0		
1.5		
2.0		
2.5		
3.0		
3.5		
4.0		
4.5		
5.0		

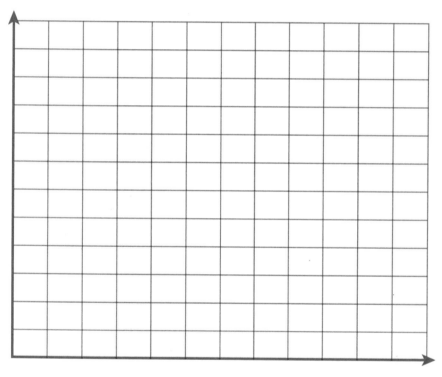

Identify three differences and three similarities between the two plots, and write them below.

Similarities:

1.

2.

3.

Differences:

1.

2.

3.

Part 2: Think about it

a. Why is it important not to have too much water in the test tube?

b. Why do you have to stir the water while heating it?

c. What was the highest reading you saw on the temperature probe?

d. Describe the temperature versus time graph. What is the difference between the two plots?

e. Was heat transferred from the heater to the water at the same rate the entire time? Was the energy transfer reduced or even stopped at some point? What evidence do you have to support your claim? (Hint: Look at the power display on the lower right of the Lab-Master screen.)

f. Why didn't the water get to the same temperature as the heater?

Part 3: Heat flow

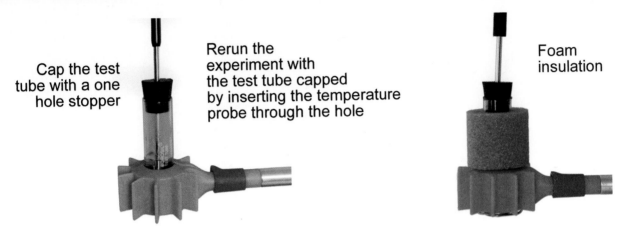

Cap the test tube with a one hole stopper

Rerun the experiment with the test tube capped by inserting the temperature probe through the hole

Foam insulation

1. Add a foam insulation ring to the test tube.
2. Put the temperature probe through a one-hole stopper so it sits below the surface of the water
3. Observe the temperature for a few minutes while the heater is set to 50°C. Does the final temperature get higher than before, or does it stay about the same?

Part 4: Thinking about what you observed

a. What was the purpose of insulating the test tube? Think about heat as energy and where the energy goes.

b. A covered pot boils much faster than an open pot. Discuss why that is and how it relates to why putting the cap on the test tube changed the maximum temperature of the water.

c. Explain why the water became warmer, even though the temperature of the heater stayed the same.

d. Explain why the *power* of the heater starts high, but drops to a very low value shortly after.

e. *Thermal equilibrium* is the situation when all temperatures have become equal. No heat flows in thermal equilibrium. Is your test tube in thermal equilibrium or not? Why do you think so? This is a hard question! Discuss it with your class and your lab group, then write up a short answer.

3D: Heat of Fusion

Why doesn't the temperature change as ice melts?

When you add heat to a sample of ice and water, the temperature doesn't change. You can see ice melt as the mixture becomes more liquid. However, as long as there is still some solid ice, the temperature stays constant. Why?

Materials
• Lab-Master with temperature probe   • Hot water (60–80°C)
• Ice   • Mass balance
• Two 8 oz foam cups

Part 1: The experiment

Attach the temperature probe.

(1)

(2) Measure the mass of about 100 g of ice into a foam cup.

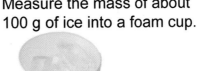

In a second cup measure about 130 g of hot water.

(3)

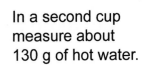

Measure and record the hot water temperature *just* before adding it to the cold ice

(4)

The temperature of the hot water must be at least 60°C

(5) Mix the hot water with the ice. Measure and record the mixture temperature after about a minute of *gentle* stirring and *after* the ice has melted.

TABLE 1. Temperature data for combining water and ice

Ice mass (g)	Ice temp. before mixing (°C)	Hot water mass (g)	Hot water temp. before mixing (°C)	Mixture temp. (°C)
	0			

Part 2: Analyzing the data

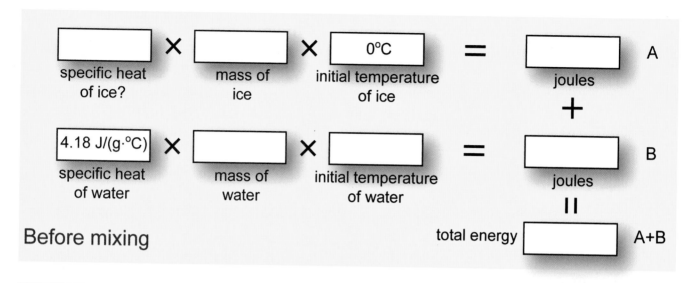

Before mixing

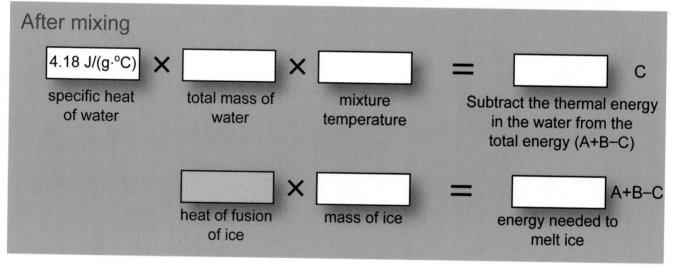

Part 3: Thinking about what you observed

a. Suggest an explanation for why the temperature of the water did *not* end up halfway between cold and hot, even though you mixed equal masses.

b. We have assumed that a temperature of 0°C represents zero thermal energy by measuring relative to the reference point of 0°C. How many joules of thermal energy did the solid ice contribute to the mixture?

c. How many joules of thermal energy did the water contribute to the mixture?

d. How does your value for the heat of fusion of ice compare to the accepted value?

e. All substances that undergo phase changes have a heat of fusion. How do other substances compare to water? Research the heat of fusion for at least four other substances.

f. Suggest an explanation for why the heat of fusion of ice is similar to or different from the other substances you chose.

4A: Phase Changes of Water

How do you change ice to water, or water to steam?

The chemical H_2O can be a solid (ice), a liquid (water), or a gas (steam). Solid, liquid, and gas are the three most common phases of matter. Water, oxygen, iron and every other chemical can exist in any of these three phases. In this investigation, you will find out exactly how to change water from one phase to another. You will also discover why you don't often find solid oxygen or gaseous iron on Earth.

> **Materials**
> - Lab-Master with temperature probe and heater
> - Crushed ice
> - 25 mm test tube
> - Boiling chips

Part 1: Setting up

① Fill the test tube about half full with crushed ice and a little water.

② Set RATE = 10 s.
Set SAMPLES = 50.

③ Heater

Set the heater to 150°C and stir constantly with the temperature probe.

④ Press **Start/Stop** to begin the experiment.

1. Place a few boiling chips in the test tube. Fill it about halfway with crushed ice and a little water.

2. Record the temperature of the ice water in Table 1 on the next page. This is the temperature at "0 minutes."

3. Set the heater to 150°C.

4. Set the Sample Rate to 10 s and the SAMPLES to 50. This will take a temperature measurement every 10 s for 500 s, which is 8.3 minutes.

5. Stir the test tube *constantly* and *gently*.

6. Watch carefully and note the time when all the ice has melted.

7. Continue watching and record the time when the water starts to boil.

Part 2: Analyzing the data

a. When the experiment is done, transfer time and temperature data for the times indicated in Table 1. Use the arrow keys on the Lab-Master to scroll back through the graph and look at the data points.

b. Plot your own graph of temperature versus time using the data from Table 1. The graph should look a lot like the graph on the Lab-Master screen.

Part 3: Thinking about what you observed

a. Describe the temperature versus time graph. Do some parts have different slopes than others?

b. Was heat energy being transferred from the heater to the water the whole time, or did the energy transfer stop at some point? What evidence do you have to support your claim?

c. Why didn't the temperature rise while there was ice in the test tube? This is a hard question! Discuss it with your group and your class before writing up your answer.

Table 1. Time vs. temperature

Time (s)	Temperature (°C)
0	
30	
60	
90	
120	
180	
240	
300	
360	
420	
500	

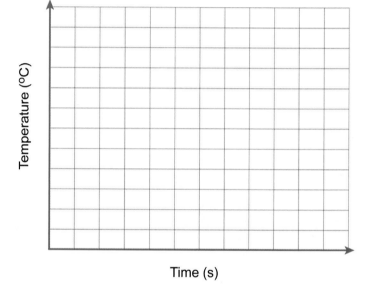

d. What was the highest reading you saw on the temperature probe? What was the water doing at that time?

e. Why did the temperature stop rising when the water started boiling? This is a hard question! Discuss it with your group and your class before writing up your answer.

Part 4: Making connections

a. Water can be written as "$H_2O(s)$," "$H_2O(l)$," and "$H_2O(g)$." What do the letters in the parentheses ( ) mean?

b. At atmospheric pressure, what is the highest temperature that liquid water can reach before it boils? Your data from Table 1 should show you the answer. Compare your results with the rest of the class and figure out the average value.

c. What is the highest temperature that ice can reach before it melts? Your data from Table 1 should show you this. Compare your results with the rest of the class and figure out the average value.

d. The two temperatures from Questions b and c above are known as the boiling point and the melting point of water. Every chemical has its own melting point and boiling point. Why don't you see solid oxygen or gaseous iron as often as you see ice and steam?

A NATURAL APPROACH TO
CHEMISTRY

4B: Indicators of Chemical Reactions

How can we tell whether a chemical reaction is occurring?

There are many ways to tell whether a chemical reaction is occurring. You have already seen many of these in your everyday life; chemical reactions happen all around you every day! In this lab, we will explore some common signs of chemical reactions, so you can learn to recognize these signs.

The signs of a reaction that are most easily observable are changes in temperature, changes in color, forming a precipitate, forming a gas, and generating light. This lab will show you a demonstration of each so you can see them for yourself.

Materials

- 20 mL vinegar
- 20 mL phenolphthalein
- 5 g of dry (anhydrous) copper sulfate powder
- 20 mL of 1 M NaOH
- 40 mL of 3% hydrogen peroxide (H_2O_2)
- 1 g iron powder
- 20 mL of 1 M $AgNO_3$
- 10 g of NaOH pellets
- 3 mL pipette
- 60 mL of water
- 30 mL of vitamin C solution
- 30 mL of 3% iodine tincture
- 10 g of starch
- Five 25 mm test tubes
- Disposable gloves
- Glass stirring rod
- Lab-Master with temperature probe

Part 1: Chemical safety rules

- This experiment will use some chemicals that should not be handled with bare hands. Wear protective gloves.

- Wear eye protection while doing these experiments

- If you spill any chemicals, inform your instructor immediately. Wash any areas of skin or clothing with cold water.

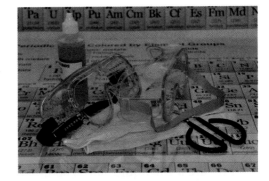

Part 2: Changes in color: hydration

1. Put 5 g of dry copper sulfate powder into a clean, *dry* test tube. Observe the color of the dry salt.

2. Pour 20 mL of water into this test tube. Observe what happens.

3. Clean out your test tubes in the sink.

Part 3: Thinking about what you have observed

a. How could you tell that a reaction occurred?

b. This is an example of a *hydration reaction*, where a dry (anhydrous) salt absorbs water. What does the word "anhydrous" mean?

c. What do you think would happen to the salt if the water were taken back out (if the solution was dried)?

Part 4: Changes in color: acid and base reactions

1. Using a pipette, place approximately 2 mL of vinegar in a test tube. The acid in vinegar is called acetic acid (CH_3COOH).

2. Add 2 or 3 drops of phenolphthalein indicator to the vinegar. Swirl to mix.

3. Using a dropper bottle, slowly add drops of 1.0 M NaOH solution to the vinegar until you see the formation of a color.

Part 5: Thinking about what you have observed

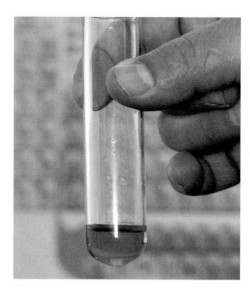

a. How could you tell that a chemical reaction occurred in this experiment?

b. What color formed in the test tube?

c. What element could have caused that color?

d. Try adding a few more drops of vinegar and record your observations. Where did the color go?

Part 6: A reaction might need time to occur

1. Put 10 mL of water in a test tube. Add 4 mL of vitamin C solution and 4 mL of iodine tincture to this test tube. The liquid should be clear.

2. Prepare a 1% liquid starch solution. (It is important to have a fresh starch solution. Do not use a solution if it is more than a day old.)

3. Put 20 mL of water in a second test tube. Add 4 mL of hydrogen peroxide and 4 mL of liquid starch solution to this second test tube.

4. Pour the contents of the second test tube into the first one. Observe the test tube for a couple minutes.

5. Wash your test tubes out in the sink.

Before   After

Part 7: Thinking about what you have observed

a. How could you tell that a chemical reaction occurred in these experiments?

b. What color formed in the test tube? What element could have caused that color?

Part 8: Precipitate formation reactions

1. Put 10 mL of water into a test tube.
2. Add 20 drops of silver nitrate ($AgNO_3$) into the test tube. (Safety note: Use gloves. Do not get $AgNO_3$ on your skin.)
3. Add sodium hydroxide (NaOH) drop by drop and observe the results.

Part 9: Thinking about what you have observed

a. How could you tell that a chemical reaction had occurred?

b. The precipitate formed is silver hydroxide (AgOH). Why do you think AgOH has a color to it whereas $AgNO_3$ does not?

Part 10: Reactions that result in temperature changes

1. Put 20 mL of water in a test tube. Measure the temperature of the water and record the value.
2. Add 4 pellets of sodium hydroxide (NaOH) using gloves and tweezers. (Safety note: *do not* touch the NaOH pellets with your bare hands.)
3. Now measure the temperature of the mixture in the test tube.

Part 11: Thinking about what you have observed

a. By how much has the temperature changed?

b. Where did the energy for the temperature change come from?

c. Why did the temperature increase?

Part 12: Gas creation

1. Pour about 20 mL of 3% hydrogen peroxide solution into a clean test tube.
2. Add a small amount of iron powder to the test tube.
3. Watch what happens. Write down any important observations.

Part 13: Thinking about what you have observed

a. How could you tell that a chemical reaction occurred?

a. Iron acts as a *catalyst* in this reaction, meaning that it is not used up. What would happen if you added more hydrogen peroxide? What about if you added more iron?

b. The gas that is created in this reaction is pure oxygen. Usually storing oxygen requires high pressure. Can you think of two places where it would be very useful to use the reaction from this experiment, because it can generate oxygen without compressing it?

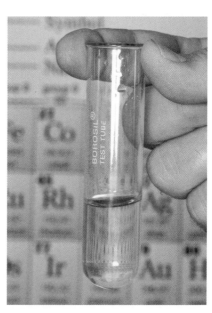

A NATURAL APPROACH TO
CHEMISTRY

4C: Chemical Changes

How can we write a chemical reaction that explains what happens during a chemical change?

New substances are made from other substances via the process of chemical change. The process of making this change is called a chemical *reaction*. In this investigation, you will explore three different types of chemical reactions. Each of the three types occurs widely in nature, in technology, and even in your own body.

Materials	
• 30 mL of 1 M HCl in a dropper bottle	• Phenolphthalein
	• Vinegar
• 30 mL of 1 M $CuSO_4$ in a dropper bottle	• Aluminum foil
	• Fine sandpaper
• 30 mL of 1 M NaOH in a dropper bottle	• Four 25 mm test tubes
	• Test tube rack
• About 5 g of zinc turnings or mossy zinc	• Erlenmeyer flask
	• 10 mL graduated cylinder

Part 1: Chemical safety rules

- Use care when working with hydrochloric acid (a strong acid) and sodium hydroxide (a strong base).

- Wear eye protection while performing these experiments.

- Avoid breathing acid fumes.

- If you spill any chemicals, inform your instructor immediately. Wash any affected areas of skin or clothing with cold water.

Part 2: Chemical reactions with aluminum

1. Lightly sand a 10 cm square piece of aluminum foil on both sides.

2. Tear the sanded aluminum in half and place the pieces in two test tubes.

3. Take two unsanded pieces of aluminum and place them in the other two test tubes.

4. Add about 3 mL of 1.0 M HCl solution to a test tube containing sanded aluminum foil, and add the same amount to a test tube containing unsanded aluminum foil. Do the same for the 1.0 M $CuSO_4$ solution in the other two test tubes.

5. Watch for at least 5 minutes and record your observations. Look for things like bubbling, warmth, cloudiness, or changes of color.

6. Answer the questions in Part 3, then clean out your test tubes in the sink.

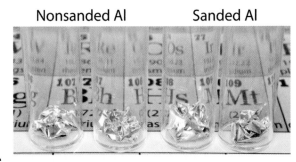
Nonsanded Al   Sanded Al

$CuSO_4$ HCl $CuSO_4$ HCl

Investigation 4C: Chemical Changes

Part 3: Thinking about what you observed

a.   Describe what happened in each of the four experiments. Write a sentence about each one.

b.   Did the sanded and the unsanded aluminum react differently in either or both solutions? Be specific.

c.   Which of the four reactions were chemical changes? Explain why you think so.

d.   The atoms on the surface of a metal tend to react with the oxygen in the air and form an oxide coating. This coating, or tarnish, appears dull and less shiny, and it decreases the ability of a metal to react. Did you observe this? Explain.

Part 4: Acid and base reactions

1.   Place approximately 2 mL of vinegar in a test tube. The acid in vinegar is called acetic acid (CH_3COOH).

2.   Add 2 or 3 drops of phenolphthalein indicator to the vinegar. Swirl to mix.

3.   Using a dropper bottle, slowly add drops of 1.0 M NaOH to the vinegar. Keep adding until a pink color persists. Write down your observations.

4.   Add 2 mL of 1.0 M HCl to a second test tube.

5.   Add 2 or 3 drops of phenolphthalein indicator to the acid. Record your observations.

6.   Using a dropper bottle, slowly add drops of 1.0 M NaOH to the acid. Keep adding drops until a pink color persists.

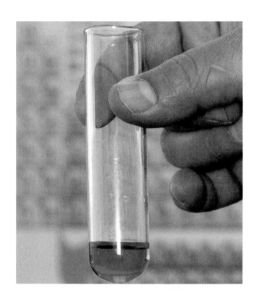

Part 5: Thinking about what you observed

a.   Describe what happened in each of the two experiments. Write a sentence about each one.

b.   Do you think chemical changes occurred in both of these experiments? Why or why not?

Part 6: Oxidation–reduction reactions

1.   Add a few zinc turnings (a pea-sized amount on your spatula) to two different test tubes.

2.   Add about 2 mL of 1.0 M HCl to one test tube, and add 2 mL of 1.0 M $CuSO_4$ to the other one. Watch for at least 5 minutes and record any observations you make. Look for things like bubbling, warmth, cloudiness, or changes in color.

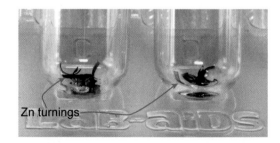

Zn turnings

Part 7: Thinking about what you observed

a.   Describe what happened in each of the experiments. Write a sentence about each one.

b.   Did these experiments represent chemical changes? Why or why not?

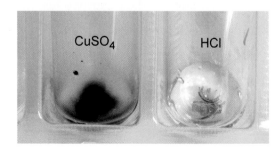

$CuSO_4$ HCl

Part 8: Precipitate reactions

1. Put 10 mL of 1.0 M CuSO₄ in the Erlenmeyer flask.
2. Put 10 mL of 1.0 M NaOH in a test tube.
3. Slowly add the sodium hydroxide (NaOH) solution to the copper sulfate ($CuSO_4$) solution. Watch for at least 1 minute and record your observations. Look for things like bubbling, motion, or changes in color.

Part 9: Thinking about what you observed

a. Describe what happened in this experiment. Write two sentences each that describe a different observation you made.

b. Was this a chemical change? Why or why not?

Part 10: Predicting products and writing chemical reactions

Here we will practice writing chemical reactions using one (or two) examples of each reaction type. The reaction types are: 1. *acid–base*, 2. *oxidation–reduction*, and 3. *precipitate*. We will go through how to write the chemical reaction for each type separately; occasionally some of the steps will be repetitive.

a. **Acid–Base:**
    Write down the chemical symbols for the reactants that you used for one experiment in Part 4. If you are not sure of the chemical formulas for some of the chemicals, look on the bottle for help. Write a forward arrow after the reactants [e.g., $HCl(aq) + NaOH(aq) \rightarrow$].

b. Split apart (dissociate) the hydrogen from the acid. $HCl(aq)$ becomes $H^+(aq)$ and $Cl^-(aq)$.
    Recall that when you split the compounds apart, the positive ion (cation) is always the one on the left, and the negative ion (anion) is written on the right.

c. Split apart the base (NaOH) into its ions, $Na^+(aq)$ and $OH^-(aq)$.

d. On the right side (products) of your arrow, you need to predict what was formed and how the atoms were rearranged. In an acid–base reaction, a salt and water are always the products. Water forms because the H^+ ion from the acid combines with the OH^- ion from the base. Essentially, the positive and negative ions on the reactants side trade partners and form products.

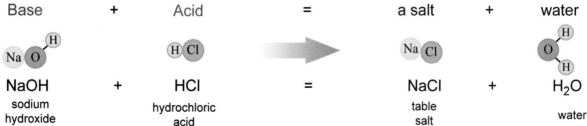

| Base | + | Acid | = | a salt | + | water |

NaOH + HCl = NaCl + H₂O
sodium hydroxide + hydrochloric acid = table salt + water

e. **Oxidation–reduction:**
    Write down the chemical symbols for the reactants that you used in one experiment in Part 6, followed by an arrow [e.g. $Zn(s) + HCl(aq) \rightarrow$].

f.   Split apart (dissociate) the compound in aqueous solution. Here, HCl(aq) becomes H^+ and Cl^-. Recall the positive ion (cation) is always the one on the left, and the negative ion (anion) is written on the right.

g.   On the right side (products) of your arrow, you need to predict what was formed and how the atoms were rearranged. Use your observations to help you determine this. Metals such as zinc and aluminum have tendencies to form positive ions and therefore lose electrons, which means they become oxidized. In this example, Zn was the metal. Did a reaction occur when Zn was placed in HCl? If so, then Zn was oxidized. Using the periodic table shown above, look up the charge of the zinc ion.

h.   If a chemical reaction did occur in Part 6, then it was a single replacement reaction, which is a type of oxidation–reduction reaction. In a single replacement reaction, the substance that appears alone (not combined with other elements) as a reactant replaces the first element in the compound. Here is an example:

$$Zn(s) + HCl(aq) \rightarrow H_2(g) + ZnCl_2(aq)$$

i.   In this case, Zn(s) replaces H^+ and combines with Cl^-. The element that was replaced is now alone in its elemental form. You do need to remember that hydrogen is a diatomic gas and that it cannot be written simply as H. It must be H_2. Zn has a 2+ charge so it requires two Cl^- ions to make it neutral.

j.   Now try predicting the products for the reaction that occurred in the second test tube in Part 6. Record your answer. This will be a single replacement reaction too.

k.   Precipitate:

Write down the chemical symbols for the reactants that you used in the experiment for Part 8, followed by an arrow. If you are not sure of the chemical formulas for some of the chemicals look on the bottle for help.

l.   Split apart (dissociate) *both* of the compounds in aqueous solution (the salts); for example, NaOH(aq) becomes Na^+ and OH^-, and $CuSO_4(aq)$ becomes Cu^{2+} and SO_4^{2-}.

m.   Now you need to predict what was formed on the products side and how the atoms were rearranged. Precipitate reactions are also referred to as "double replacement" reactions. This simply means the positive and negative ions trade partners.

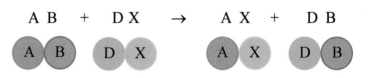

n.   Use the example above to predict the products of your reaction. Later in the course you will learn that group 1 metals and nitrate are "spectator ions," meaning they never form precipitates or solids. This will allow you to guess what the chemical formula for your solid is.

A NATURAL APPROACH TO
CHEMISTRY

5A: Inside the Atom

What is inside an atom?

People once thought atoms were the smallest possible particles of matter. Then even smaller particles were discovered inside atoms! The structure of the atom is the underlying reason that nearly all the properties of matter we experience are what they are.

Materials
• Atom model
• Proton, neutron, and electron marbles
• Isotope periodic table (Appendix A)

Part 1: Setting up

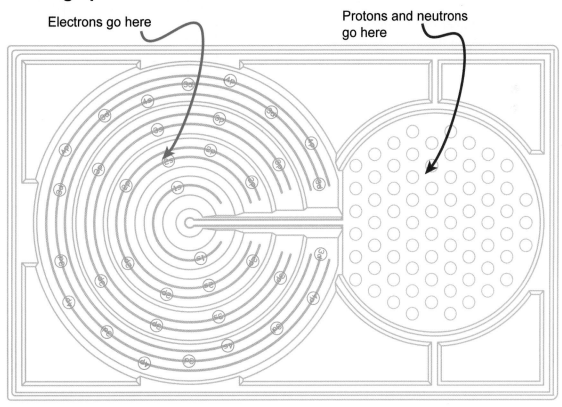

Electrons go here

Protons and neutrons
go here

The atom model represents the particles inside an atom and how they are arranged.

1. Find the element lithium (Li) on the periodic table.

2. Use the colored marbles to build a lithium atom.

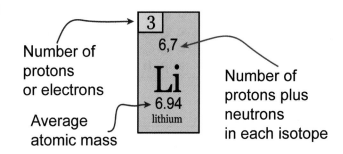

Number of protons or electrons

3

6,7

Li

6.94

lithium

Average atomic mass

Number of protons plus neutrons in each isotope

Part 2: Thinking about the atom

a. What is the number of protons or electrons called?

b. In the lithium atom, what are the numbers 6 and 7 called?

c. Why do some elements have more than one number above the symbol? What are the variations in this number called?

Part 3: Atom building

1. Using the atom model, build the following elements: He, C, and O. What do you notice about the number of protons and neutrons?

2. Now build the following elements: Na, Al, and P. What do you notice about the number of protons and neutrons?

3. Now build the following elements: Sc, V, and Mn. What do you notice about the number of protons and neutrons?

4. Plot the number of protons versus the number of neutrons on the graph.

5. What pattern do you notice about the number of protons versus the number of neutrons as the mass of the atom gets bigger?

6. Now look at some large elements such as Pa, Pb, Bi, and U on the periodic table. How do the numbers of protons and neutrons compare to each other? Did you notice the same pattern as shown on your plot?

TABLE 1. Components of Nuclei

Element	Protons	Neutrons
He		
C		
O		
Na		
Al		
P		
Sc		
V		
Mn		

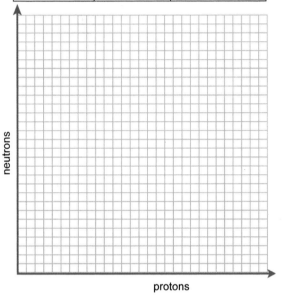

neutrons

protons

Part 4: The average atomic mass

One class has eight different groups. Each group makes its own version of an atom of the same element. Here are their results:

	①	②	③	④	⑤	⑥	⑦	⑧
	e p n	e p n	e p n	e p n	e p n	e p n	e p n	e p n
Individual atomic mass								

a. What element were the students building?

b. Fill in the atomic mass of each of the eight atoms.

c. Calculate the average atomic mass for the class.

d. How does your average compare with the average atomic mass listed in the periodic table? Is it more, less, or about the same as the average mass listed in the periodic table?

e. What must be different about the natural abundances of the two different isotopes compared to what was built in this class?

A NATURAL APPROACH TO
CHEMISTRY

5B: Spectrophotometry

How is color measured?

Color is an important part of life and chemistry. Dyes are chemicals that create color by absorbing light. If it seems odd that you can create color by taking away light, do this investigation and you will be surprised!

Materials
• Five clean cuvettes • Cuvette stand
• Four different types of food • Lab-Master
coloring (red, green, blue, and • Four 25 mm test tubes
yellow) • 3 mL pipettes
• Tap water

Part 1: Preparation of solutions

1. Put 1 drop of each food coloring in each test tube.
2. Add 10 mL of water to each test tube and mix.
3. Using the pipette, take 3 mL of each solution and put it in the cuvettes. You should have four cuvettes, each with a different color.
4. Now put 3 mL of water in the fifth cuvette. This cuvette will be used as a reference in your measurements.

Part 2: Absorption and color

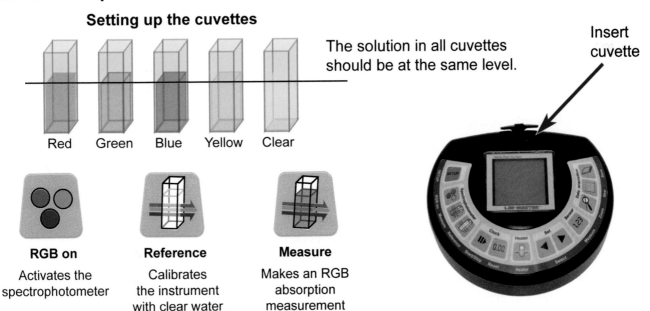

Setting up the cuvettes

The solution in all cuvettes should be at the same level.

Insert cuvette

Red   Green   Blue   Yellow   Clear

RGB on
Activates the spectrophotometer

Reference
Calibrates the instrument with clear water

Measure
Makes an RGB absorption measurement

1. Activate the spectrophotometer of your Lab-Master by pressing the **RGB** button.
2. Use the clear cuvette and the **Reference** button to calibrate the spectrophotometer.
3. Measure the RGB values for each cuvette, including the clear reference cuvette and record your data in Table 1 under the "1 drop of color" column.

Table 1: Spectrophotometer data in absorbance units (AU)

Cuvette	1 drop of color			2 drops of color			3 drops of color		
	R	G	B	R	G	B	R	G	B
Red									
Green									
Blue									
Yellow									
Clear									

Part 3: Increasing the concentration

We will now increase the concentration of the colors in the solutions.

1. Discard the solutions in the test tubes and the cuvettes.
2. Rinse the test tubes, cuvettes, and pipettes with clean water.
3. Add 2 drops of each food coloring to each test tube.
4. Repeat Steps 2–4 of Part 1.
5. Take absorption measurements of the new solutions by repeating the steps in Part 2.
6. Record your data in Table 1 under the "2 drops of color" column.
7. Repeat the entire procedure once more by adding 3 drops of food color in the test tubes. Record the data in Table 1 under the "3 drops of color" column.

Part 4: Things to think about

a. Explain what the values of R, G, and B mean in terms of the energy of light.

b. Is white light a color, or is white light a mixture of all colors? How do you know? How can you test this?

c. Explain the diagram on the right. How is the color green produced?

d. Which color was absorbed most strongly by the yellow dye? Which colors were transmitted more? Why do you think so?

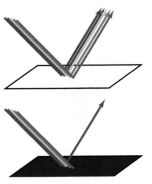

e. Make a graph showing how absorption changes with one, two, and three drops of food coloring. You can plot all four colors on the same graph. You can either do this by hand on graph paper or by using the SD card in the Lab-Master and graphing the results on the computer.

f. What does the absorbance of R, G, and B tell us about the way the yellow color in our experiment is made?

g. What do you notice about the way that the R, G, and B absorbance values change for each solution? Do the dye molecules in food color absorb a single color of light or a range of colors? How do you know?

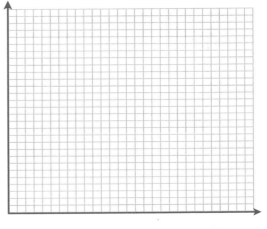

h. Research the way color books and magazines are printed. Explain the acronym CMYK. Why do printers use CMYK color instead of RGB?

5C: Spectroscopy

How is color used to identify elements?

When atoms absorb or emit light, they do so by moving electrons from one energy level to another. Since the energy levels in atoms are discrete, the light comes out in discrete colors, called spectral lines. The exact values of energy for each energy level are different for different elements. That means each element has its own unique signature, called a *spectrum*. A spectrum is like an energy "fingerprint" that identifies each element.

Materials
• Element spectroscopy cards (one set per group)

Part 1: The spectrum cards

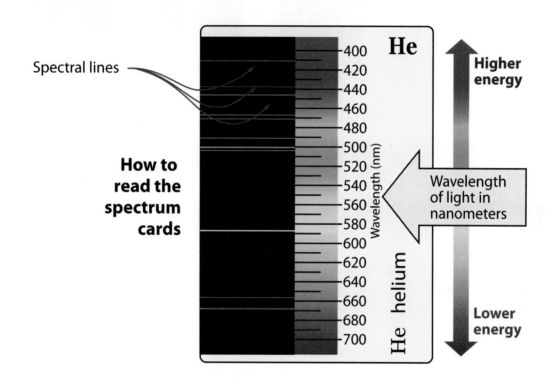

Part 2: Learning to use the spectrum cards

a. Which element has a signature of three spectral lines grouped together at 655 nm?

b. Which element has a double line near 584 nm?

c. Which element has a gap between 500 and 610 nm with no spectral lines in between?

d. Which element has the fewest spectral lines of all the elements on the cards? Can you suggest a reason why this element has the fewest number of spectral lines?

e. Do you notice a pattern between the atomic mass of an element and the number of spectral lines?

Part 3: Spectral identification

Spectral lines are characteristic signatures for each element. When elements are combined, they retain their spectral signatures. If elements are mixed, the combined spectrum shows the lines of each separately. Scientists can use the patterns of lines to identify each element present in the mix. Try it for yourself. Use the cards to solve the following puzzles.

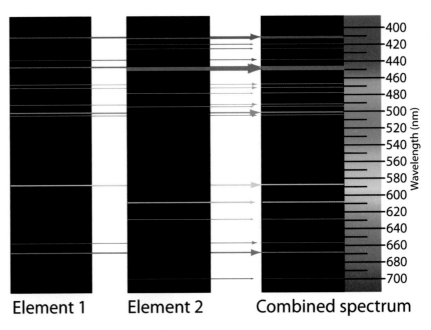

Element 1   Element 2   Combined spectrum

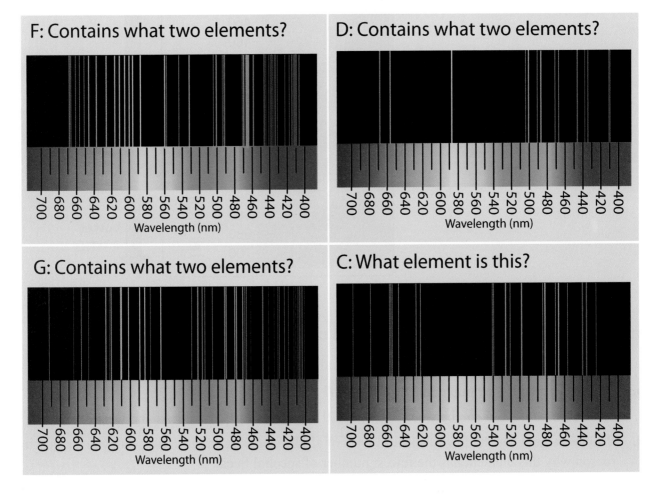

F: Contains what two elements?

D: Contains what two elements?

G: Contains what two elements?

C: What element is this?

Part 4: Thinking about what you have learned

Astronomers use the same technique you just used to figure out the age of stars. How can they use the spectral lines coming from a star to figure out its age? You may have to research this topic online.

A NATURAL APPROACH TO
CHEMISTRY

6A: Periodic Table Riddles

Can you identify the element in each riddle? You may have to identify a particular isotope for certain riddles.

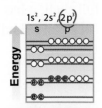

1. This atom generally forms up to three bonds with other atoms. It has 14 particles in its nucleus. It is also the major constituent of the air we breathe.

2. This atom has its second energy level completely filled. It has an odd (not even) mass number. It also lights up the night sky in Las Vegas.

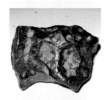

3. This transition metal is lighter than zinc and has an average atomic mass closest to its second lightest isotope. It is the most common element found in meteorites, one of which is shown here.

4. This radioactive atom has six electrons and eight neutrons. It is used to determine the age of many objects up to tens of thousands of years old.

5. This atom has three electrons in its third energy level. Its mass number is one plus twice its atomic number. If aircraft were made of steel instead of this element, they would be too heavy to fly.

6. This alkali earth element has six stable isotopes. It both strengthens bones and regulates heartbeat in many animals, including humans.

7. There are two ways to build the nucleus of this element. Both have masses greater than one, and it is the only element where one isotope has more protons than neutrons. It can be used to make energy in a nuclear fusion reaction, and scientists have considered getting it from the Moon because there is so little on Earth.

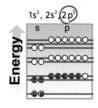

8. This atom has only one stable isotope and five electrons in its outermost shell. It is the most electronegative element, and it is added to our tap water to help prevent tooth decay.

9. This element has an average atomic mass of 6.94 amu. This particular isotope has four neutrons. The atomic mass of its most common isotope and its effects on the human brain gave the drink "7-UP" its name.

10. This atom has one fewer electron than it needs for a full shell, it has a mass number of 36, and it is radioactive. It is often used to keep large bodies of water free of bacteria.

11. This atom has an average atomic mass only 0.09 amu heavier than its lightest stable isotope.

12. This atom is a transition metal with an odd atomic number less than 36. It has two stable isotopes; the lighter one has an abundance of 73% compared to the heavier one.

13. This element chemically combines with three hydrogen atoms. Its only stable mass number is one more than twice its atomic number. It is also the key element in the molecules in our body that store and release energy.

14. This transition metal has a smaller atomic mass than iron. It has three stable isotopes with even mass numbers and one with an odd mass number. This element is also what makes "stainless steel" stainless.

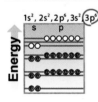

15. This element forms no chemical bonds. All of its stable isotopes have even mass numbers. It is often used during welding to keep the metal clean.

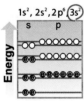

16. This metal combines with one oxygen atom. All of its stable isotopes have mass numbers that only differ by 1. It oxidizes very easily, and campers use this to their advantage to start fires even in wet conditions.

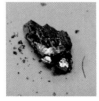

17. This group 2 element has only one stable isotope. It is the lightest structural element in existence, and because of this it is used in satellites to keep their weight low. It is also very poisonous.

A NATURAL APPROACH TO
CHEMISTRY

6B: Periodic Table Fill In the Blank

Can you fill in the missing squares of the periodic table (on the next page) by using the properties given for each element?

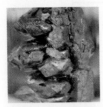

1. Calcium (Ca) only combines with one oxygen atom, and it has a low electronegativity. When it is placed in water, it releases hydrogen gas.

2. Helium (He) is the lightest noble gas, and it has a full valence shell. It is now exclusively used in blimps after it was discovered that hydrogen is too flammable.

3. Germanium (Ge) can either lose or gain four electrons to have a filled outer shell. It is a special type of semiconductor that converts electricity directly to light, and it is used in making many types of LEDs and solid state lasers.

4. Cobalt (Co) is a transition metal. The blue color of its salts gives us the color "cobalt blue," and one of its radioactive isotopes (cobalt 60) is used as an x ray source in dentistry.

5. Boron (B) can lose three electrons to have a filled outer shell. It is used in the control rods in nuclear reactors because it absorbs neutrons. This makes boron a good control mechanism for nuclear reactions.

6. Arsenic (As) can chemically combine with three hydrogen atoms. It is very poisonous and has been used as a poison since medieval times.

7. Sodium (Na, from *natrium*) has only one electron in its outer shell. This makes it very reactive; putting sodium in water causes so much hydrogen and heat to be released that it can explode violently.

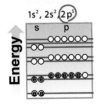

8. Fluorine (F) is the most electronegative atom on the periodic table. It is so corrosive that only certain containers can hold it. Pure fluorine gas would react with exposed skin so quickly that it would appear to melt.

Isotope Periodic Table
(first four rows)

Key

6	Atomic number
12, 13	Mass numbers of stable isotopes
C	Element symbol
12.01	Average atomic mass
carbon	Element name

Group 1	Group 2		Group 13	Group 14	Group 15	Group 16	Group 17	Group 18
1 1,2 **H** 1.01 hydrogen								**2**
3 6,7 **Li** 6.94 lithium	**4** 9 **Be** 9.01 beryllium		**5**	**6** 12,13 **C** 12.01 carbon	**7** 14,15 **N** 14.01 nitrogen	**8** 16,17,18 **O** 16.00 oxygen	**9**	**10** 20,21,22 **Ne** 20.18 neon
11	**12** 24,25,26 **Mg** 24.31 magnesium		**13** 27 **Al** 26.98 aluminum	**14** 28,29,30 **Si** 28.09 silicon	**15** 31 **P** 30.97 phosphorus	**16** 32,33,34 36 **S** 32.07 sulfur	**17** 35,37 **Cl** 35.45 chlorine	**18** 36,38,40 **Ar** 39.95 argon
19 39,41 **K** 39.10 potassium	**20**		**31** 69,71 **Ga** 69.72 gallium	**32**	**33**	**34** 74,76,77 78,80,82 **Se** 78.95 selenium	**35** 79,81 **Br** 79.90 bromine	**36** 78,80,82 83,84,86 **Kr** 83.80 krypton

21 45 **Sc** 44.96 scandium	**22** 46,47,48 49,50 **Ti** 47.88 titanium	**23** 51 **V** 50.94 vanadium	**24** 50,52,53 54 **Cr** 51.00 chromium	**25** 55 **Mn** 54.94 manganese	**26** 54,56,57 58 **Fe** 55.85 iron	**27**	**28** 54,56,57 58 **Ni** 58.69 nickel	**29** 63,65 **Cu** 63.55 copper	**30** 64,66,67 68,70 **Zn** 65.39 zinc

Name:_____ Section:_____ Date:_____

6C: Valence

Why is the periodic table shaped the way it is?

Once people started to isolate pure samples of a number of elements, curious patterns started to emerge. The element beryllium combines with twice as much oxygen as lithium. Magnesium also combines with twice as much oxygen as lithium, sodium, and potassium. In fact, lithium, sodium, and potassium all behave similarly to each other and differently from most other elements. Beryllium, magnesium, and calcium are similar to each other and different from the rest of the elements. What is the explanation for why certain "groups" of elements are chemically similar to each other? The answer has to do with the arrangement of the electrons. The electron arrangement affects the chemical properties of atoms. The position of an atom on the periodic table is also directly related to its electron arrangement. In this investigation, we will learn about the electron structure and its role in the formation of chemical compounds.

Materials
• Atom model
• Proton, neutron, and electron marbles

Part 1: Setting up

Build an oxygen atom as shown the diagram below.

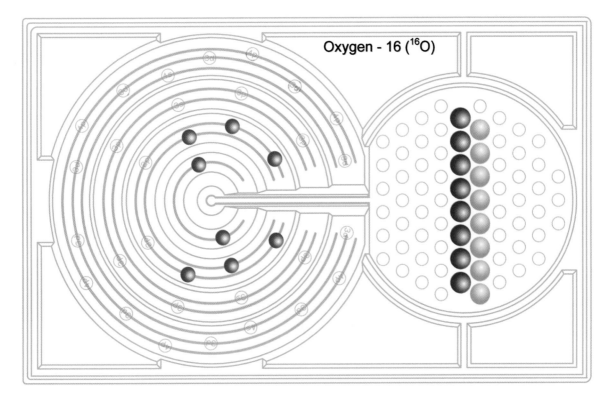

Oxygen - 16 (^{16}O)

Part 2: What makes oxygen act like oxygen?

a. The overall energy in an atom is *lowest* when its outer shell of electrons is either completely filled or completely empty. What can an oxygen atom do to achieve this preferred state?

b. Which of the two choices (outer shell filled or outer shell empty) do you think lowers the energy of an oxygen atom the most?

Part 3: Chemical bonding

Make two hydrogen atoms, and put them on either side of the oxygen atom.

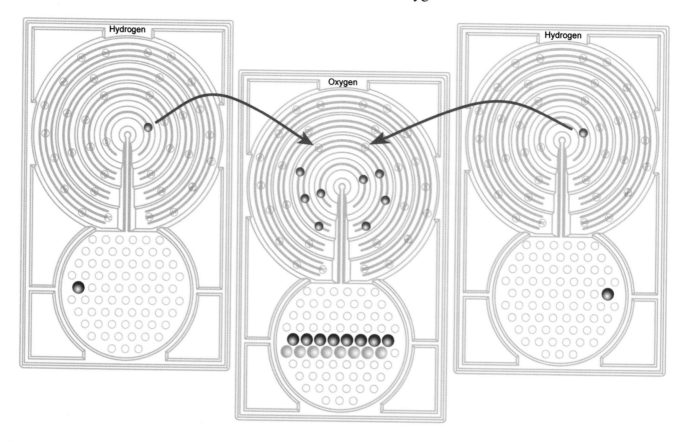

Use what you did (and the diagram) to explain why the chemical formula for water is H_2O and not H_3O, H_3O_2, or some other combination of hydrogen and oxygen.

Part 4: Valence

Chemical bonds between atoms only involve the electrons in the outer, unfilled shells. These electrons are called *valence electrons*.

Build two different atoms that each have two, three, four, seven and eight valence electrons.

Answer questions a–d for each atom you built.

a. What element is this atom?

b. Would it be more likely to accept or give up electrons to make bonds?

c. Where on the periodic table is it?

d. How would it combine with hydrogen and with oxygen?

Table 1. Valence electrons

Valence electrons	Elements
2	
3	
4	
7	
8	

7A: Lewis Structures

Why do molecules have specific compositions and shapes?

Atoms combine to form molecules to lower their energy. Atoms that combine have a lower total energy together as a molecule than they do apart as pure elements. Atoms combine to form molecules by sharing electrons. Since the atoms of each element have unique electronic structures, different elements form different bonds.

Materials
• Molecular modeling set

Part 1: Introduction to Lewis Dot Diagrams

The diagram below shows Lewis diagrams and valence electrons for the first ten elements. Elements form chemical bonds to reach a stable configuration of eight valence electrons.

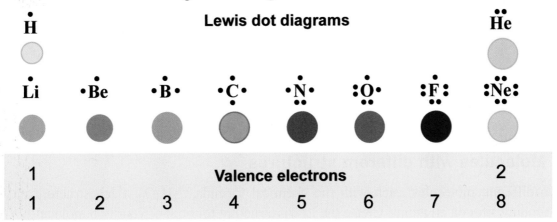

a. How many bonds should a hydrogen atom normally make?

b. How many bonds should a lithium atom normally make?

c. How many bonds should a carbon atom normally make?

d. How many bonds should a nitrogen atom normally make?

e. How many bonds should an oxygen atom normally make?

Part 2: Molecules and Lewis structures

Build the following molecules from their Lewis dot structures.

(1)
```
    H H
H:C:C:O:H
    H H
```
Chemical
formula _____

Common
name _____

(2)
```
:O::O:
```
Chemical
formula _____

Common
name _____

(3)
```
  :O:
H:C:H
```
Chemical
formula _____

Common
name _____

(4)
```
        H
:Cl:C::C:Cl:
        H
```
Chemical
formula _____

Common
name _____

Investigation 7A: Lewis Structures

Part 3: Lewis structures from models

Build the four molecular models shown in the pictures below. Create Lewis dot structures, chemical formulas, and structural diagrams for each one.

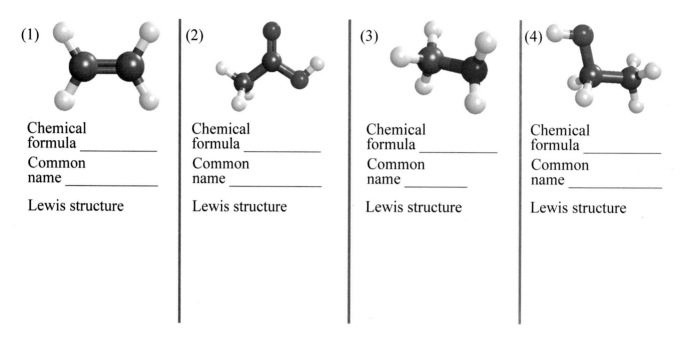

(1) Chemical formula ___ Common name ___ Lewis structure

(2) Chemical formula ___ Common name ___ Lewis structure

(3) Chemical formula ___ Common name ___ Lewis structure

(4) Chemical formula ___ Common name ___ Lewis structure

Part 4: Molecules with different structures

Create two different molecules, each with the chemical formula $C_2H_4O_2$. Each structure must use all available bonding sites on all atoms. Create the Lewis structure for both of your two molecules.

$C_2H_4O_2$
Can you make two different compounds with this chemical formula?

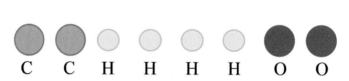

C   C   H   H   H   H   O   O

Name		
Structural diagram		
Lewis structure		

A NATURAL APPROACH TO
CHEMISTRY

7B: The Geometry of Molecules

How do molecules form in three dimensions?

Chemical formulas tell you very little about the shape of a molecule. Structural diagrams are better, but they are still flat. Real molecules have three-dimensional forms that are created by the shapes of the electron orbitals in atoms. This investigation will look at some of the fundamental molecular shapes and the elements that produce them.

Materials
• Molecular modeling set

Part 1: Linear and bent molecules

Build these six molecules.

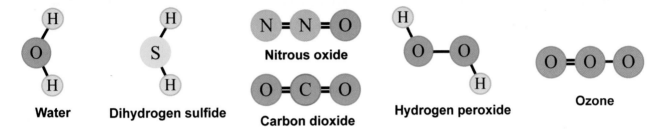

| Water | Dihydrogen sulfide | Carbon dioxide | Hydrogen peroxide | Ozone |

Compounds made of only two or three atoms are typically either bent or linear in shape, respectively.

a. Name two other elements which would likely form a bent molecule when bound with two hydrogen atoms.

b. Name two other elements that would likely make a linear molecule when combined with silicon in a ratio of 2:1 (element:silicon).

Part 2: Trigonal planar and trigonal molecules

Molecules containing four or more atoms can be planar or pyramidal. Build the following molecules.

Ammonia
NH_3

Formaldehyde
CH_2O

a. Which of these molecules has a trigonal pyramidal shape? How do you know?

b. Which of these molecules has a trigonal planar shape? How do you know?

c. Name another element which would combine with three hydrogen atoms to make a trigonal molecule.

Part 3: Hydrogen and carbon molecules

A carbon atom can form four single bonds. Carbon can also make double and triple bonds, both to other elements and to itself. This makes carbon the most versatile element in the periodic table. Carbon has four valence electrons; this means it can just as easily contribute four electrons to achieve a completely empty energy level, or it can gain four electrons to get to a completely full energy level. To get a sense of some of the shapes carbon can make, build the following molecules.

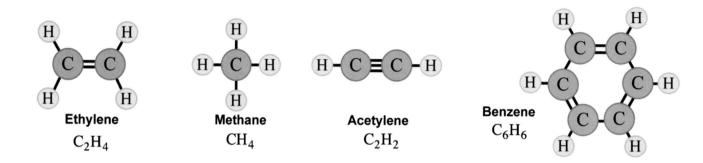

a.   Which of these molecules (if any) is planar?

b.   Which of these molecules (if any) is linear?

c.   Which of these molecules (if any) is tetrahedral? A tetrahedron is a pyramid with four triangular sides.

d.   Which of these molecules is a ring?

Part 4: Nitrogen and oxygen molecules

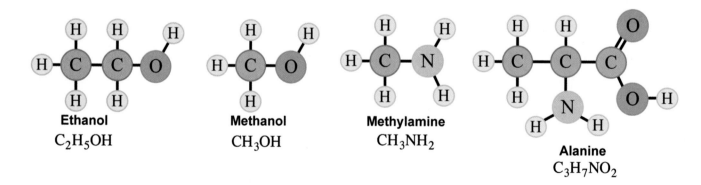

a.   Name two of these molecules that are tetragonal. What element is central to these molecules?

b.   Name two of these molecules that are trigonal. What element is central to these molecules?

c.   Describe similarities between methanol (wood alcohol) and ethanol (grain alcohol).

d.   Amines are nitrogen–bearing compounds, often with very strong odors. Which of these compounds are amines?

A NATURAL APPROACH TO
CHEMISTRY

8A: The Formula of a Hydrated Salt

How do you figure out a chemical formula?

Chemical formulas are determined in a lab by performing experiments. Some chemical formulas include attached water. This investigation will show an example.

Materials
• Hydrated copper sulfate
• Desiccator
• Mass balance
• Lab-Master system with temperature probe and heater

Part 1: Dehydrating a salt

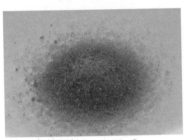

Hydrated
solid
copper sulfate

$CuSO_4 \cdot x\,H_2O$

Anhydrous
solid
copper sulfate

$CuSO_4$

In hydrated copper sulfate each ion has a fixed number of water molecules attached to it

A *hydrate* is an ionic compound, also known as a salt, with water molecules incorporated into its crystal structure. There is water inside a hydrate, even though the compound is a solid! In this experiment, we will use a hydrate of copper, called copper(II) sulfate ($CuSO_4 \cdot xH_2O$), where x represents the number of water molecules in the crystal per formula unit of $CuSO_4$. Hydrated copper sulfate is blue, whereas dry (or *anhydrous*) copper sulfate is white. By heating a known mass of the hydrate to remove the water and weighing the remaining salt, we can determine the mass percentage of water in the hydrate and also the value of x in the formula of the hydrate.

1. Record the mass of the empty desiccator.

2. Add 4.0 g of blue (hydrated) copper sulfate, and record the total mass.

3. Put the desiccator in the heater. Set the heater temperature to 150°C. Use the temperature probe to slowly stir the powder until it all turns from blue to white. Periodically record the temperature.

4. Weigh the desiccator again with the anhydrous white salt and record the final mass. Dispose of the salt in the labeled waste container.

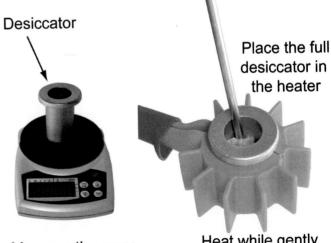

Desiccator

Measure the mass of the desiccator empty and full

Place the full desiccator in the heater

Heat while gently stirring until the powder turns completely white

Table 1. Mass data for Part 1

	Mass (g)
Desiccator (empty)	
Desiccator and hydrated (blue) salt	
Desiccator and anhydrous (white) salt	

Part 2: Data analysis

a. Calculate the mass of hydrate used.

b. Calculate the mass of water removed by subtracting the mass of dried hydrate from the mass of hydrate you started with.

c. Calculate the formula mass for water.

d. How many moles of water were driven off by the heat?

e. Calculate the formula mass for $CuSO_4$.

f. Assume the dried hydrate is pure $CuSO_4$. How many moles are there in your sample?

g. Calculate the value for x, rounded to the nearest whole number.

$$x = \frac{\text{moles of } H_2O}{\text{moles of } CuSO_4}$$

h. Write your formula for the hydrate.

Part 3: Error analysis

If you had a "perfect" mass balance, your calculation for x would be as perfect as your experimental technique would allow. Unfortunately, real balances have a minimum *resolution*. The resolution is the smallest mass that the balance can accurately measure.

a. How does the resolution of the balance affect your results?

b. What is the smallest mass your balance can measure? Call this value e, the measurement error.

c. The real masses could range from $(m - e)$ to $(m + e)$. Complete the following table by calculating the minimum and maximum masses of the hydrated and dried copper sulfate.

Table 2. Error analysis

	Measured mass, m (g)	Estimated error, e (g)	m − e (g)	m + e (g)
Mass of hydrated $CuSO_4$				
Mass of dried $CuSO_4$				

d. Calculate the *most* water the hydrate could have contained. This would be the largest possible value $(m + e)$ for the hydrated $CuSO_4$ minus the least possible value $(m - e)$ for the dried $CuSO_4$.

e. Calculate how many moles of water that Part d represents. Calculate the value of x using this result.

f. Repeat the calculation for the *least* amount of water that the hydrate could have contained. This is the smallest mass $(m - e)$ of hydrated $CuSO_4$ minus the largest mass $(m + e)$ of dried $CuSO_4$.

A NATURAL APPROACH TO
CHEMISTRY

8B: Naming Chemical Compounds

How do we name different chemical compounds?
What do chemical names on labels mean?

When you read the labels on toothpaste, shampoo, antacids, deodorant, nasal spray, mouthwash, or sunscreen products (just to name a few), you may notice some common ingredients. In this investigation, we will practice writing chemical formulas for the names you may recognize on the labels of some common household items. We will also build molecular models of some compounds based on their names. Finally, we will practice making simple sketches of some ionic compounds. Given their formulas, we will predict their names.

Materials

- Household items: sunscreens, toothpastes, shampoos, mouthwash, antacids, skin creams, and baking soda
- Molecular modeling kit
- Colored pencils

This investigation is designed to help you learn and practice how to name binary ionic and molecular compounds. Let's see whether different brands of household products use similar ingredients that you can recognize. We will use some polyatomic ions, but we will not focus on chemical naming for compounds containing more than two elements.

Part 1: Naming simple chemicals in household items

1. Select some common household items for your group. If your instructor had you bring some in, work with those items.

2. Read the ingredients on the label (both active and inactive). Focus on simple chemical names that look familiar. For some products, there will be several ingredients that have complicated chemical names. You may skip those for now. (Optional: If you wish later, you can select one and research it on the Internet to see what the chemical formula is for that compound.)

3. Write down the formula(s) for the active ingredient(s).

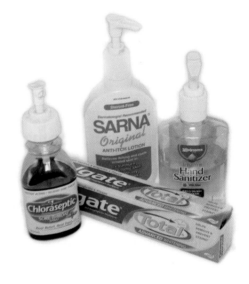

NaF: sodium fluoride

Part 2: Building models from chemical names

Here we know the name of the chemical compounds, and we will use molecular models to build them. Use the table below to guide you in this section.

Table 1. Chemical names

Name of substance	Chemical formula	Lewis structure	Sketch of model (3D)
phosphorus trichloride			
dihydrogen monoxide			
boron trifluoride			
carbon disulfide			
ammonium ion			
nitrate ion			

Part 3: Sketching ionic compounds

1. Ionic compounds are composed of a metal and a nonmetal. We cannot use covalent bonds to represent these compounds, because they do not share electrons. Given the name of each ionic compound, write the chemical formula.

2. Use the formula to make a sketch of your compound. Like MgF_2 on the right, use circles to represent the ions. Place one ion in each circle, and be sure to show the charges on the ions.

MgF_2: magnesium fluoride

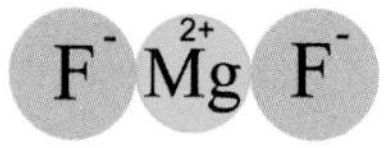

Part 4: What did you learn?

1. What is different about naming molecular and ionic compounds?

2. What is the same about naming molecular and ionic compounds?

3. What is the "common name" for dihydrogen monoxide?

4. List the formulas for two more polyatomic ions. Select two that are different from the ones used in Part 2.

A NATURAL APPROACH TO
CHEMISTRY

9A: Density and Concentration

How much sugar is in the soda you drink?

Sodas vary widely in the amounts of sugar they contain. Does this contribute to their different flavors? In this investigation, you will determine how much sugar is in different brands of soda. You will do this by determining the densities of different sodas and comparing them to a calibration curve that you will create with pure sugar and water mixtures.

Materials
• Four 8 oz foam cups
• Bag of granulated sugar
• Glass stirring rod
• Variety of sodas: colas, citrus, ginger ale, etc.
• Distilled water bottle
• 100 mL graduated cylinder
• Mass balance

Part 1: Determining the amount of sugar in soft drinks

Choose three nondiet sodas to see how the sugar contents vary. Perform a taste test to see which tastes the sweetest. Write down your hypothesis.

Preparing your four concentrations of solution

5.0 g sugar
95.0 g of water

10.0 g sugar
90.0 g of water

20.0 g sugar
80.0 g of water

40.0 g sugar
60.0 g of water

1. Place an empty cup on the balance and zero it. Label this cup "5.0 g in 100 g."

2. Pour 5.0 g of sugar into the cup. Fill it with hot water until there is 100.0 g of solution.

3. Stir until the sugar is dissolved.

4. Place a plastic 100 mL graduated cylinder on the balance and zero the balance.

5. Using the solution you prepared in Steps 2 and 3, fill the graduated cylinder to 40 mL. Record both the mass and volume as accurately as you can in Table 1.

6. Repeat Steps 1–5 above using 10.0, 20.0 and 40.0 g of sugar in 100 grams of solution.

7. Calculate and record the percent sugar and the density of the solutions in Table 1.

Measure the volume and mass of each solution using the graduated cylinder on the balance

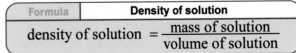

Formula	Percent concentration of sugar
	$\% \text{ sugar} = \dfrac{\text{mass of sugar}}{\text{total mass}} \times 100$

Formula	Density of solution
	$\text{density of solution} = \dfrac{\text{mass of solution}}{\text{volume of solution}}$

TABLE 1. Sugar solution density data

Initial		Percent sugar (% mass)	Graduated cylinder		Density (g/mL)
Sugar (g)	Solution (g)		Volume (mL)	Mass (g)	

Part 2: Making a calibration curve

a. Graph the density versus the amount of sugar. Use a ruler to get the best–fit line, or do a linear regression on the computer. This will be your reference curve.

b. Determine the reported density of sugar in each soda by reading the amount from the label of the soda can.

c. Use the graduated cylinder to measure the mass of 100 mL of each of the three sodas. Loosely cover your test tubes with plastic wrap to minimize evaporation. Let the soda sit overnight so that it becomes flat (degassed).

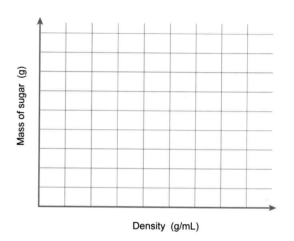

d. Determine the density of each soda using the density formula.

e. Using your graph, determine the amount of sugar in each of your sodas. Do the results support your hypothesis? Compare different soda brands.

Part 3: Density of diet versus regular soda

Use flat or degassed soda to get the best result.

1. Use the graduated cylinder to measure the mass of 100 mL of diet soda.
2. Calculate the density of diet soda using $d = m/v$.
3. Compare the densities of the diet and regular soft drinks.

Part 4: What did you learn?

a. Describe what you learned about different brands of soft drinks.

b. Which one contained the most sugar?

c. Do you think the results would have been different if you used carbonated soda? How might this have changed your results? Explain.

d. In your opinion, what is the largest source of error in this lab?

e. How much soda do you drink a day? How much sugar do you consume from soda each day?

A NATURAL APPROACH TO
CHEMISTRY

9B: Solutions and Beer's Law

How can we quickly find the concentration of a solution?

Beer's Law states that the absorbance of a solution (A) is directly proportional to its concentration (M). Beer's Law can be written as $A = kM$, where k is a proportionality constant. You will first determine the linear relationship between absorbance and molarity for a known concentration of $CuSO_4$. You will then use this relationship to construct a *calibration curve*. The standard curve will be used to determine the concentration of an unknown molarity of copper(II) sulfate.

Materials

- Six cuvettes
- 50 mL of 1.0 M $CuSO_4$(aq)
- Two 100 mL graduated cylinders
- Pipette
- Marking pencil or labeling tape
- Lab-Master
- Distilled water
- Six 25 mm test tubes
- Test tube rack

Part 1: Preparing your solutions

1. Solution A: Measure approximately 50 mL of 1.0 M $CuSO_4$(aq) in your 100 mL graduated cylinder. Fill a small test tube about halfway and label this "1.0 M." This is solution A in test tube A.

2. Solution B: Add 25 mL of 1.0 M copper sulfate solution to an empty 100 mL graduated cylinder. Fill to the 50 mL mark with water. Stir and transfer enough to fill a test tube half full. Label this test tube B.

3. Solution C: Start with 25.0 mL of Solution B in your 100 mL graduated cylinder. Fill to the 50 mL mark with water. Stir and transfer enough to fill a test tube half full. Label this test tube C.

4. Solution D: Start with 25.0 mL of solution C in the graduated cylinder. Fill to the 50 mL mark with water. Stir and transfer enough to fill a test tube half full. Label this test tube D.

5. Solution E: Start with 25.0 mL of solution D in the graduated cylinder. Fill to the 50 mL mark with water. Stir and transfer enough to fill a test tube half full. Label this test tube E.

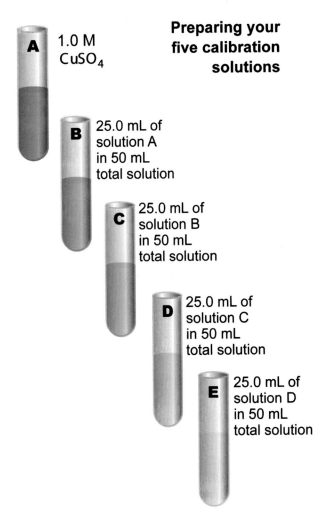

Preparing your five calibration solutions

A — 1.0 M $CuSO_4$

B — 25.0 mL of solution A in 50 mL total solution

C — 25.0 mL of solution B in 50 mL total solution

D — 25.0 mL of solution C in 50 mL total solution

E — 25.0 mL of solution D in 50 mL total solution

Note: This process of cutting the concentration each time is called a *serial dilution*.

Investigation 9B: Solutions and Beer's Law

Part 2: Collecting data

Place 3 mL of each solution into a clean cuvette. Add 3 mL of distilled water into a sixth clean cuvette. This will be used for your reference measurement. Start by performing the calibration using the reference cuvette. Next, insert a cuvette of each of the five solutions into the spectrophotometer. Measure and record the RGB absorption for each solution. This will provide the data that you will use to construct your calibration curve. Be sure that your cuvettes are clean. If your cuvettes are not dry, rinse them once with a little of the solution you are about to measure, discard the rinse solution and fill the cuvette with 3 mL of the appropriate solution.

RGB on
Activates the spectrophotometer

Reference
Calibrates the instrument with clear water

Measure
Makes an RGB absorption measurement

Table 1. Absorption data

Solution	R	G	B
A			
B			
C			
D			
E			

Insert cuvette

Part 3: Determining your concentrations

You may already realize that a serial dilution cuts your concentration by one half its original amount. Let's go through how you can determine your concentration.

1. For solution B (first dilution),
   the original molarity is $M_A = 1.0$ M, and the volume is $V_A = 25.0$ mL.
   We are solving for the new molarity (M_B).
   The final volume is $V_B = 50$ mL, so

$$M_B = 1.0 \ M \times \left(\frac{25 \ mL}{50 \ mL}\right)$$

2. Use the same process for the rest of your test tube dilutions C, D, and E, and fill in the molarity column in Table 2. Transfer your absorption data into the R, G, and B columns of Table 2.

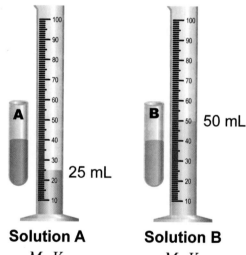
Solution A   **Solution B**
M_1, V_1 M_2, V_2

Dilution formula
$$M_1V_1 = M_2V_2 \ \rightarrow \ M_2 = M_1\left(\frac{V_1}{V_2}\right)$$

$$M_B = M_A\left(\frac{25 \ mL}{50 \ mL}\right)$$

$$M_B = 0.5 \ M$$

Table 2. Concentration and absorption data

Solution	Molarity of CuSO$_4$	Absorbance Units (AU)		
		R	G	B
A				
B				
C				
D				
E				

Part 4: Calibration curve

Make a graph by hand on the graph paper on the next page (or by computer) that plots absorbance units (AU) versus molarity (M). Give your graph a title like "Calibration Curve for Copper Sulfate." Label the axes and give the units.

Part 5: Determining the unknown

1. Obtain 10 mL of the unknown solution of $CuSO_4$ provided by your instructor. Put it in a clean cuvette, and make certain that the liquid is at the same level as the other cuvettes.

2. Measure the absorbance for R, G and B of this unknown solution. You may need to do a dilution if the concentration is too high. Ideally, to be most accurate, you want an absorbance reading between 0.5 and 3.5.

3. Plot the R, G, and B values on your calibration curve. Read down to determine the concentration of your unknown $CuSO_4$ solution.

Part 6: Thinking it through

A calibration curve for a particular solution is very useful once it is constructed. Doctors and laboratories use this method to measure body fluid concentrations. Body fluid concentrations such as blood and urine can be analyzed for a particular chemical in this way. Chemists use calibration curves to reliably determine unknown concentrations of a particular solution.

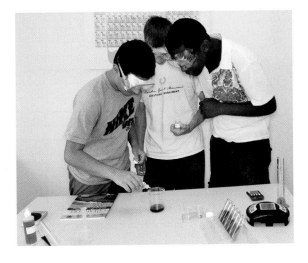

1. Do you think this is a reliable method for determining the concentration of a known solution?

2. What would likely be the largest source of error? Explain.

3. If you were to repeat this experiment, do you think you would get better results?

4. How do your results for the unknown compare to those of your classmates?

RGB Absorbance vs. concentration

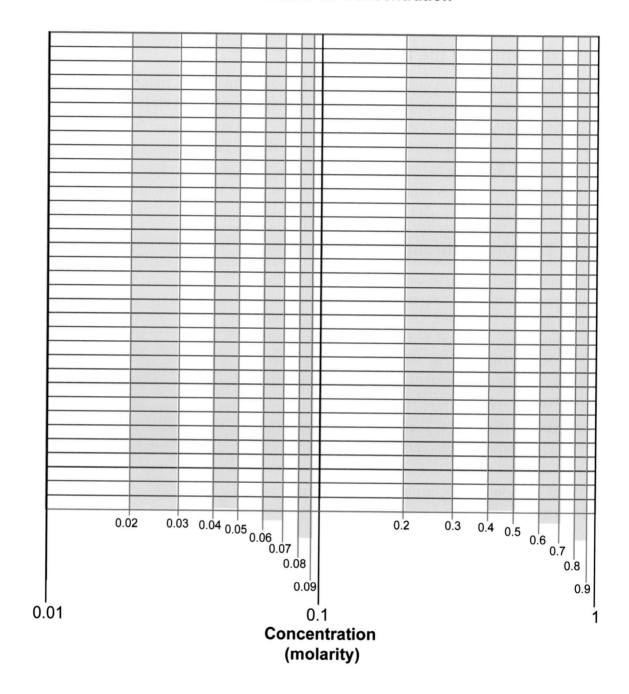

Absorbance units (AU)

Concentration
(molarity)

0.01   0.02   0.03   0.04   0.05   0.06   0.07   0.08   0.09   0.1   0.2   0.3   0.4   0.5   0.6   0.7   0.8   0.9   1

A NATURAL APPROACH TO
CHEMISTRY

9C: Solution Calorimetry

How do you measure the energy change in a solution?

When acid and base solutions are mixed, a *neutralization reaction* occurs. The neutralization reaction yields heat, water, and salt as products. Depending upon the molar amounts, there may also be some unreacted acid or base left over. In these experiments, you will use a *coffee cup calorimeter* to collect your data. The heat of solution will be determined in kilojoules per mole of NaOH. The basic scientific principle behind this investigation is energy conservation. The foam cup closely resembles an isolated system, and so its total energy is conserved.

Materials

- Two 8 oz nested foam cups with lids
- 1.0 L of 1.0 M HCl
- 1.0 L of 1.0 M NaOH
- 3.0 g vial of NaOH pellets
- Distilled water bottle
- 100 mL graduated cylinder
- Mas balance
- Lab-Master with temperature probe

Part 1: Procedure A

1. Weigh your empty double foam cup calorimeter assembly. Add about 45.0 mL of 1.0 M HCl and reweigh.

2. Measure 40.0 mL of 1.0 M NaOH. Be sure you have less NaOH than HCl.

3. Record the temperature of each solution before mixing to within 0.1°C using your temperature probe. Pour the NaOH solution into the calorimeter with the HCl. Immediately place the cover over the mixture. Stir gently and record the highest temperature reached.

4. Weigh the combined solutions in the cup, and then pour the mixture down the sink. Rinse the cup thoroughly (three or four times) with tap water. Dry the inside and outside of the coffee cup calorimeter for the next reaction.

Part 2: Procedure B

1. Weigh the double foam cups, and then zero the balance. Add about 100.0 mL of distilled water and record the mass. (It is a good idea to know the mass of the foam cups.)

2. Weigh your vial of solid NaOH pellets. Record the weight of the NaOH vial. Tap the vial to be sure the pellets are still loose.

3. Record the temperature of the water in your foam calorimeter. Add half of your pellets directly to the water by tapping the vial. The exact amount of NaOH(s) does not matter. However, try to add approximately half of the pellets. Replace the lid on the vial immediately! The pellets will absorb moisture from the air. **Warning:** *Avoid* contact with the NaOH pellets! If you do accidentally touch them, wash your hands with plenty of water. NaOH is caustic and can cause skin irritation.

4. Cover the calorimeter. Stir gently until all of the pellets have dissolved and the highest temperature has been reached. Record this temperature.

5. Pour the mixture down the sink and rinse the cups thoroughly (three or four times) with tap water. Dry the inside and outside of the cup for the next reaction.

Part 3: Procedure C

1. Weigh the double foam cups. Zero the balance. Add about 100.0 mL of 1.0 M HCl and weigh. Record the mass.

2. Weigh and record the weight of the half empty vial of NaOH pellets.

3. Record the temperature of the HCl solution in your calorimeter.

4. Add the remaining NaOH pellets to the HCl and place the cover on your calorimeter. Stir until all of the pellets are dissolved and the highest temperature has been reached.

5. Weigh and record the weight of the empty vial of NaOH.

6. Pour the mixture down the sink and rinse your cups thoroughly.

Mass of empty vial _____

Mass of full vial _____

Mass of half–full vial _____

Mass of NaOH used
in Part 2 of Procedure B _____

Mass of NaOH used
in Part 3 of Procedure C _____

Part 4: Calculating the heat of solution

1. Write a balanced chemical equation including physical states (s, l, g, or aq) for each of the three reactions in Procedures A, B, and C.

2. Here we will calculate the heat of solution ($\Delta H_{solution}$) using the equation:

Formula	**Heat of solution**

$$\Delta H_{solution} (J) = \left[\text{mass (g)}\right] \times \underbrace{\text{(specific heat of solution)}}_{\text{use } C_P \text{ of water} \left[\text{J/(g·°C)}\right]} \times \Delta T \ (°C)$$

You may assume that the solutions have the same specific heat as water [4.18 J/(g·°C)].

3. Substitute your data for each of the three reactions A, B, and C into the equation above and calculate the heat of solution.

4. Write the reaction as you did in Part 1, and place the heat you have calculated next to it. Label it with its appropriate unit of joules (J).

5. Next, convert joules to kilojoules by dividing by 1,000. For each experiment, determine the number of moles of NaOH that you used. Divide the kilojoules in each reaction by the moles of NaOH used for each reaction. This is your heat of solution ($\Delta H_{solution}$).

6. Write out each reaction with the $\Delta H_{solution}$ value next to each one.

Part 5: What did you learn?

a. Describe what you learned about neutralization reactions in this investigation.

b. In your opinion, what is the largest source of error?

c. How do your heats of solution compare to those obtained by other groups? Explain.

d. What was the least precise measurement you made when collecting your data? Explain.

e. Why do we need to calculate $\Delta H_{solution}$ per mole of NaOH? Explain.

10A: Discovering the Solubility Rules

What aqueous solutions form solids when mixed?
What type of chemical reaction is this?

Sometimes when you mix two aqueous salt solutions, one of the products formed is a solid called a *precipitate*. The ions in solution that do not form a precipitate are called *spectator ions*. In this laboratory, you will see that some ions in solution are *soluble* and that others are *insoluble*. The insoluble ions form a solid precipitate in solution.

Materials

- Well plate or 10 small test tubes
- 30 mL dropper bottles of 0.10 M salt solutions
- Salt solutions (0.10 M) of $NaNO_3$, $NaOH$, $NaCl$, Na_2SO_4, Na_2CO_3, $Cu(NO_3)_2$, $NH_4(NO_3)$, KNO_3, and $AgNO_3$
- Distilled water bottle

Part 1: Procedure

1. Using the data in Table 1 provided below as a guide, mix 2 or 3 drops of each solution listed across the top with 2 or 3 drops of each solution listed down the side. Mix each pair of solutions one at a time. Be careful to keep track of which ones you are mixing.

Table 1. Solubility data table

	$NaNO_3$	$NaOH$	$NaCl$	Na_2SO_4	Na_2CO_3
$NaNO_3$					
$Cu(NO_3)_2$					
NH_4NO_3					
KNO_3					
$AgNO_3$					

2. Record the color and consistency of each precipitate that forms from mixing two solutions. If there is no precipitate, then write "no reaction." When your well plate is full (or your test tubes are all used), dispose of the waste in the waste container. Follow this by rinsing once in the sink with distilled water. Dry your well plate with a paper towel. Continue to test each combination of salt solutions.

Part 2: Writing the chemical equations

a.   Refer to your table and write down the reactant solutions for one mixture that resulted in a precipitate [e.g., $NaOH(aq) + AgNO_3(aq) \rightarrow$].

b.   Separate the reactant ions [e.g., $Na^+(aq) + OH^-(aq) + Ag^+(aq) + NO_3^-(aq) \rightarrow$]. Recall that cations are positive (+) and anions are negative (−).

c.   Now switch the places for the cations and anions. This is called a *double replacement* or a *metathesis reaction*.

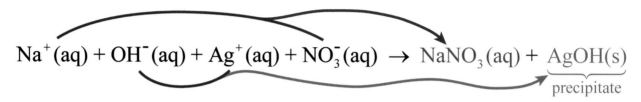

d.   Look carefully at your observations in the data table. Notice any patterns that may be helpful. Based on your data, write down one or two sentences describing how you can tell which ions form the solid precipitates you observed. We show the solid precipitate by labeling it (s) instead of (aq).

e.   Repeat steps 1–4 for each of the different combinations that yielded a precipitate upon mixing. Note that there will be times when you need to balance your chemical reactions. This will occur when you are using a divalent cation such as Cu^{2+} and a monovalent anion such as OH^-. In this case you will need to make sure your charges add to zero, as in $Cu(OH)_2$.

Part 3: Solubility rules

Based on your results, we will develop a set of "solubility rules." These rules will be in the form of a general statement that describes which ions are soluble and which are insoluble. These rules will apply to the limited number of tests you performed but will also be useful in making future predictions.

1.   Describe which anions form insoluble or soluble compounds. For example, if all nitrates are soluble when mixed with Na^+, K^+, Cu^{2+}, NH_4^+, Ag^+ and Ni^{2+}. In this case, we could make the general statement that nitrates are soluble, because they did not form precipitates.

2.   Make a list of your solubility patterns. Look for similarities.

3.   Compare your results and rules with those from another group.

Part 4: Identifying an unknown salt solution

1.   Test the unknown salt solution provided by your instructor. Record your observations.

2.   Using the data you collected and your list of rules, try to identify the ions in the unknown solution.

3.   Write out the chemical reaction that you think occurred for your unknown solution.

A NATURAL APPROACH TO
CHEMISTRY

10B: Chemical Reactions

How can we identify the products in a chemical reaction? How can we write what we observe as a chemical reaction?

In this investigation you will carry out a variety of chemical reactions. You will have the opportunity to observe all sorts of chemical changes. By taking careful observations before, during, and after the reactions, you will be able to predict the products that are formed. After you have a good idea what the products are, you can then practice writing out the chemical equation that represents each reaction you performed.

Materials

- Cu strips
- Mg ribbon
- Wax candle
- Tongs
- Watch glass
- Metal spatulas
- Calcium oxide
- Distilled water bottle
- Six 25 mm test tubes
- 1.0 M HCl
- 1.0 M KOH
- Lab-Master system with heater
- Desiccator
- Copper(II) carbonate

- 10 g of ammonium carbonate [$(NH_4)_2CO_3$]
- Cobalt(II) chloride paper
- Phenolphthalein
- Stirring rod
- Wooden splint
- Matches
- Lime water
- 10 g of baking soda ($NaHCO_3$)
- Calcium metal (optional)
- Rubber tubing attached to a glass rod inserted into a rubber stopper that fits the test tube

Part 1: Chemical safety

- Use caution when handling the acid (HCl) and the base (KOH). These substances are caustic and can burn your skin. If you do come in contact with them, rinse your hands with running tap water for 3–5 minutes.

- Always wear goggles.

- Never breathe chemical fumes.

- If you spill any chemicals, inform your instructor immediately.

Part 2: Reactions of metals

1. Metal and Air:
   Heat a small strip of copper metal in the flame of a candle for 2–3 minutes. Make observations about how the metal looks before and after heating. Place the piece of copper on your watch glass and scrape off some of the coating. Make some observations.

2. Metal and water (optional):
   Fill a test tube about halfway with distilled water. Add a small piece of calcium metal to the test tube. When the reaction appears to be over, gently touch the test tube and record how it feels. Write down any observations. Add two drops of phenolphthalein and make more observations. Rinse the contents of the test tube into the sink with tap water.

3. Metal oxide and water:
    Fill a clean test tube with about 2 in of distilled water. Add a small
    spatula (pea-sized amount) of calcium oxide to the test tube, and
    mix the contents with a stirring rod. Make some observations. Add
    2 drops of phenolphthalein and record more observations. Rinse
    the contents of the test tube into the sink with tap water.

4. Metal and acid:
    Add about 1.5 in of 1.0 M HCl to a clean test tube. Place the test
    tube in the test tube rack. Add a small strip of Mg ribbon to the
    test tube. Quickly place a second test tube of the same size over
    the top of the first test tube to collect the gas. Hold the test tubes
    close together so that no gas escapes. When the Mg ribbon is done
    reacting, have your lab partner light a wooden splint. Put the
    flaming splint in the mouth of the top test tube. Record your
    observations. Rinse the contents of the test tube into the sink with
    tap water.

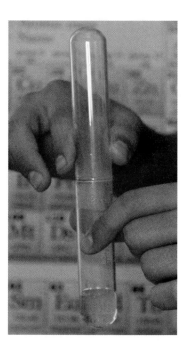

Part 3: What happened?

a. What gases in air could react with copper? Which one do you think reacted the most?

b. What do you think the coating on the copper in Part 1 was? Explain.

c. What does the phenolphthalein tell you about the solution in Part 3?

d. What did the flaming splint do when it was introduced to the test tube in Part 4? Why do you think
this happened?

Part 4: Decomposition Reactions: Testing for gaseous products

1. Baking soda (sodium bicarbonate)
    Add about 10.0 g of baking soda to a dry test tube.
    Attach a one-hole stopper and a rubber tubing assembly
    to the mouth of the test tube. Place the end of the rubber
    tubing into the bottom of a second test tube containing 2
    in of lime water. Place the test tube containing the
    baking soda in the Lab-Master heater as shown in the
    picture on the right.
    Set the heater to 120°C and observe to see if bubbles
    start to appear in the lime water. If you see no bubbles
    within a minute or two, increase the heater temperature
    to 150°C for a faster response. Watch the lime water as
    the bubbles continue to pass through it. Remove the
    rubber stopper from the test tube, and hold a piece of
    cobalt chloride paper into the mouth of the test tube.
    Record your observations in your lab notebook. Allow
    the test tube to cool for 5 minutes. Discard the solid
    $NaHCO_3$ and rinse the test tube in the sink.

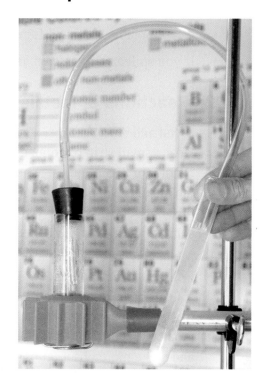

2. Ammonium carbonate:
    Add about 10.0 g of ammonium carbonate [$(NH_4)_2CO_3$] to a dry test tube. Place the test tube in the heater of the Lab-Master. Set the heater to 70°C. Watch the test tube and its contents as they heat. You may need to turn the heat up another 10–30°C to get the reaction to occur. After 1–2 minutes, look for condensation to begin to form on the sides of the test tube. When this occurs you may smell the odor of ammonia. Hold a piece of cobalt chloride paper down inside the test tube and note any color change. Try to avoid touching the sides of the test tube with the paper. Continue heating and place a flaming splint into the mouth of the test tube. What happens to the splint? Is there any solid left after heating? Let the test tube cool before cleaning it with water.

3. Metal carbonate:
    Add about 1.0 g of copper(II) carbonate ($CuCO_3$) to the desiccator. Describe the appearance of the powder. Set the heater to 150°C and heat it for a few minutes. Do you notice a color change? We know that when $CuCO_3$ is heated, it decomposes according to the following reaction:

    $$CuCO_3(s) \xrightarrow{heat} CuO(s) + CO_2(g)$$

    CuO is copper oxide, which has a black color. This reaction is not taking place in your desiccator if the color does not change from green to black. What is the main reason for this? What would you do differently to make sure that this reaction occurs?

Part 5: Thinking about it

a. What happened to the flaming splint when you placed it into the mouth of the test tube in the reaction of Part 4.1?

b. What gas do you think the flaming splint was testing for? Briefly explain.

c. What color did the cobalt chloride paper turn? Cobalt chloride paper turns pink in the presence of moisture or water vapor.

d. What color was the cobalt chloride paper initially?

e. Was there any other evidence that water vapor may have been produced?

f. Each of the three experiments produced the same gas. Can you guess what that gas was? Explain.

g. Can you guess which of the three experiments produced ammonia? Explain your reasoning.

Part 6: Acid–base reactions

Neutralization: Add about 2.0 mL of 1.0 M HCl to a small test tube. Add 2 or 3 drops of phenolphthalein to the acid and swirl to mix. Now add 1.0 M KOH drop by drop from a dropper bottle. Record the total number of drops that you add. Swirl the test tube after the addition of each drop of KOH. Record your results. Keep adding the KOH until a pink color persists after swirling.

Part 7: Thinking about it

a. What happens to the acid solution color when KOH is added?

b. How many drops did the solution require to change color?

c. Compare your results with those of other groups. Was yours the same? Explain in a couple of sentences why they may or may not have required the same number of drops to change color.

Part 8: Writing chemical reactions

a.   Make a list that includes each of the four reactions you carried out in Part 2. As you list each reaction, write out the chemical formulas for each of the reactants. If you are not sure about some of the formulas, look on the label of the bottle for help. Also label the physical states of the reactants: (s), (l), (g), or (aq).

b.   Try to predict the products of each reaction. To do this you will need to carefully assess your observations. Write out any products you are sure of based on the tests you performed. Look at your reactants to see whether all of the elements have been used to form products. If not, think about what other product(s) may have been formed. Here is an example of MgO reacting with water.

$$MgO(s) \ + \ H_2O(l) \quad \rightarrow \ Mg(OH)_2\,(aq)$$

metal oxide +   water $\rightarrow$ base

c.   Compare your results with another group.

d.   Make a list that includes each of the three reactions you carried out in Part 4. As you list each reaction, write out the chemical formulas for each of the reactants. If you are not sure about some of the formulas, look on the label of the bottle for help. Also label the physical states of the reactants: (s), (l), (g), or (aq).

e.   Try to predict the products of each reaction. To do this you will need to carefully assess your observations. Write out any products you are sure of based on the tests you performed. Look at your reactants to see whether all of the elements have been used to form products. If not, think about what other product(s) may have been formed. The general form of the approach is shown below.

| | moisture
water vapor | extinguished
splint | look at what
is left over |

$$Reactants \quad \rightarrow \quad H_2O(l) \ + \ CO_2\,(g) \ + \ \underline{\hspace{2cm}}$$

f.   Compare your results with those of another group.

g.   Identify each of the gases you tested for. How were you able to determine which gas was which? Explain.

10C: Calorimetry: Hess's Law

How do you use calorimetry to measure the heat of chemical reactions?

Hess's law allows us to indirectly determine the heat of a chemical reaction. This means we can determine the heat of a chemical reaction without performing the experiment directly. We can use calorimetry to calculate the heat of chemical reactions in solution. Once we know the ΔH values for the reactions, we can then manipulate these equations and add them together to determine the heat of formation of a substance that is involved in these reactions. In this experiment, we will determine the heat of formation of magnesium oxide (MgO) by measuring the energy associated with reactions that result in its formation. The total energy in the system that contains the MgO is conserved. The energy changes are path independent, so it does not matter how the MgO is formed. In this investigation we will use our data to prove Hess's law.

Materials

- Two 8 oz nested foam cups with lids
- 150 mL of 1.0 M HCl
- 0.6 g of magnesium ribbon
- 1.0 g of magnesium oxide
- Distilled water bottle
- 100 mL graduated cylinder
- Mass balance
- Lab-Master with temperature probe

Part 1: Metal and acid.

1. Weigh your empty double foam cup calorimeter assembly. Add about 60.0 mL of 1.0 M HCl and reweigh.

2. Record the temperature of the HCl.

3. Weigh approximately 0.6 g of Mg ribbon.

4. Carefully add the Mg ribbon to your calorimeter containing the acid. Immediately place the cover over the mixture. Stir gently and record the highest temperature reached.

5. When the reaction is complete, pour the mixture down the sink. Rinse the cup thoroughly (three or four times) with tap water. Dry the inside and outside of the coffee cup calorimeter for the next reaction.

Part 2: Metal oxide and acid

1. Weigh the empty double foam cups. Add about 60.0 mL of 1.0 M HCl solution and reweigh. Record your mass.

2. Record the initial temperature of the HCl.

3. Weigh 1.0 g of MgO.

4. Add the MgO to your calorimeter containing the HCl.

5. Cover the calorimeter and stir gently until all of the MgO has reacted. Record the highest temperature reached.

6. Pour the mixture down the sink and rinse the cups thoroughly (three or four times) with tap water. Dry the inside and outside of the cup for the next reaction.

Part 3: Finding the heat of formation (ΔH_f^o) of MgO

1. Write a balanced chemical equation, including physical states (s, l, g, or aq) for each of the reactions in Parts 1 and 2.

2. Calculate the heat of reaction (ΔH_{rxn}) using the following equation:

Formula	Heat of Reaction

$$\Delta H_{rxn}\,(\text{J}) = \big[\text{mass (g)}\big] \times \underbrace{(\text{specific heat of solution})}_{\text{use } C_P \text{ of water } \big[\text{J/(g·°C)}\big]} \times \Delta T\,(\text{°C})$$

In this equation, the mass is the total mass of the solution acid and Mg or acid and MgO, the specific heat is that of water, and the change in temperature is ΔT. You can assume that all of the solutions have the same specific heat as water [4.18 J/(g·°C)]

3. Substitute your data for each of the two reactions into the equation above and calculate your heat of reaction.

4. Write the reaction as you did in Part 3.1, and place the heat you have calculated next to it. Label it with its appropriate unit of joules (J).

5. Next, convert joules to kilojoules by dividing by 1,000. For each experiment, determine the number of moles of solid that reacted (Mg ribbon or MgO); this is your limiting reactant. Divide the kilojoules for each reaction by the moles of Mg (Part 1) or MgO (Part 2) used for each reaction. This is your heat of solution (ΔH_{rxn}).

6. Write out each reaction with the ΔH_{rxn} value next to each one.

7. Look up the standard heat of formation (ΔH_f^o) for liquid water in a standard heat of formation table in the *Natural Approach to Chemistry* textbook or online.

8. (Optional:) Use Hess's Law to determine ΔH_f^o for MgO and compare your value with the accepted value. The relevant reactions are
    I. Mg(s) + 2HCl(aq) → MgCl$_2$(aq) + H$_2$(g)
    II. MgCl$_2$(aq) + H$_2$O(l) → MgO(s) + 2HCl(aq)
    III. H$_2$(g) + 1/2O$_2$(g) → H$_2$O(l)
    These equations can be algebraically manipulated to add up the formation reaction of MgO(s):
    $$Mg(s) + 1/2O_2(g) \rightarrow MgO(s)$$

Part 4: What did you learn?

a. Describe what you learned about calorimetry reactions in this investigation.

b. In your opinion, what is the largest source of error?

c. How do your heats of reaction for Parts 1 and 2 compare to those of other groups? Explain.

d. What was the least precise measurement you made when collecting your data? Explain.

e. Why do we need to calculate ΔH_{rxn} per mole of solid (Mg or MgO)? Explain.

11A: Stoichiometry

How much of any chemical is used or produced in a reaction?

Suppose a doctor prescribed a medicine but forgot to tell you how much to take? Take too little and the medicine won't work. Take too much and it could harm or even kill you. Knowing the proper amount is crucial to medicine, and to chemistry in general. This experiment will show you how scientists determine the precise amounts of chemicals used or produced in chemical reactions.

Materials

- Mass balance
- Two 8 oz plastic cups or 100 mL beakers
- Two 16 oz plastic cups or 250 mL beakers
- At least 50 g of baking soda (sodium bicarbonate, $NaHCO_3$)
- At least 200 mL of vinegar (acetic acid, $HC_2H_3O_2$) (normal 5% strength, not low acidity)

Part 1: The reaction

Add 10.0 grams of
NaHCO3

Add 30.0 grams
of vinegar

Slowly add the
vinegar to the
baking soda

1. Put an empty cup on the balance and zero it. Measure 10.0 g of baking soda in the cup. Record the measured mass in Table 1 (row 1).

2. Put another empty cup on the balance and zero it. Measure 30.0 g of vinegar in the cup. Record the measured mass in Table 1 (row 2).

3. Add the masses of vinegar and baking soda, and record the sum in Table 1 (row 3).

4. Slowly pour the vinegar into the baking soda. Record the mass after the reaction stops (row 4).

Table 1: Reaction data

Step	Balance reading (g)
1: mass of baking soda	
2: mass of vinegar	
3: total mass (vinegar + baking soda)	
4: total mass after combination and after the reaction is done	

Investigation 11A: Stoichiometry

Part 2: What happened?

a. What evidence did you observe that indicated a chemical reaction was taking place?

b. Explain the difference in the total mass before and after mixing.

c. Do you see any baking soda that has not reacted?

Part 3: Understanding the reaction

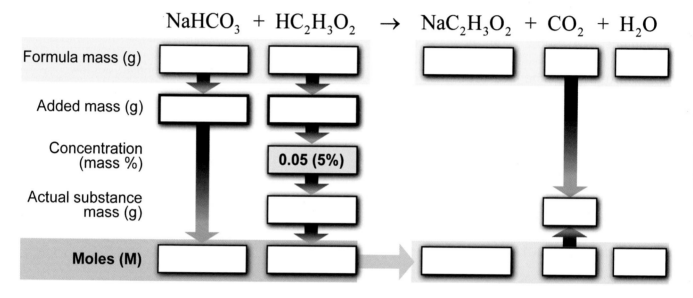

$$NaHCO_3 + HC_2H_3O_2 \rightarrow NaC_2H_3O_2 + CO_2 + H_2O$$

a. The balanced reaction is written on the first line of the chart above. Calculate the formula mass of each of the products and reactants.

b. One of the products is a gas. Which one? Will this product's mass contribute to the mass as measured on the balance after the reaction has finished? Why or why not?

c. On the second line (Added mass), write down the mass of the baking soda and vinegar you added.

d. Since vinegar is 5% acetic acid, multiply the vinegar mass by its concentration (0.05) to get the actual mass of acetic acid.

e. Use the formula masses to calculate the moles of $NaHCO_3$ and $HC_2H_3O_2$.

f. Use the balanced equation to determine how many moles of CO_2 were produced.

g. Calculate the mass of CO_2 produced in the reaction using the formula mass of CO_2.

Part 4: Stop and think

a. How many grams of CO_2 were produced in the reaction?

b. How does the answer to Part a explain the mass measurement you found at the end of the experiment?

c. Did all the baking soda react? How do you know?

d. Did all the acetic acid react? How do you know?

e. What was the limiting reactant in this experiment? How do you know?

84

Part 5: Making an efficient reaction

If you were reacting baking soda and vinegar as a chemist, you would want enough vinegar to completely react with the baking soda. Use the next chart to calculate that amount.

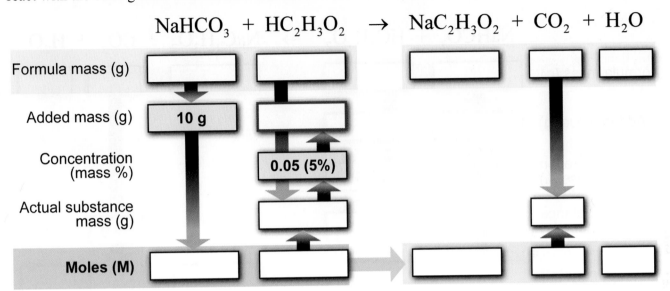

$$NaHCO_3 + HC_2H_3O_2 \rightarrow NaC_2H_3O_2 + CO_2 + H_2O$$

a. Calculate the number of moles in 10.0 g of $NaHCO_3$.

b. How many moles of acetic acid are needed to exactly neutralize the baking soda?

c. Use the formula mass to calculate the mass of acetic acid in grams.

d. Divide the mass of acetic acid by 0.05 (since vinegar is 5% acetic acid) to get the mass of vinegar you need (red box).

e. Calculate how many grams of CO_2 this reaction will produce.

f. Predict the total mass of the liquid and solid reactants and products together. This is the mass that will be measured on the balance.

Part 6: Test your hypothesis

1. Measure out 10.0 g of baking soda in one cup.
2. Measure out the required amount of vinegar (from the red box above) in the other cup.
3. Write down the total mass before you mix the reactants.
4. Mix the reactants by *slowly* adding the vinegar to the baking soda a little at a time. Stir gently for several minutes while the reaction proceeds.
5. When all the bubbling has stopped, record the total mass of the product solution.

Table 2: Reaction data

Step	Balance reading (g)
1: mass of baking soda	10.0
2: mass of vinegar	
3: total mass	
5: total mass after reaction is complete	

Part 7: Using stoichiometry

In this part, you are going to calculate how much baking soda and vinegar you would need to make 10 g of CO_2.

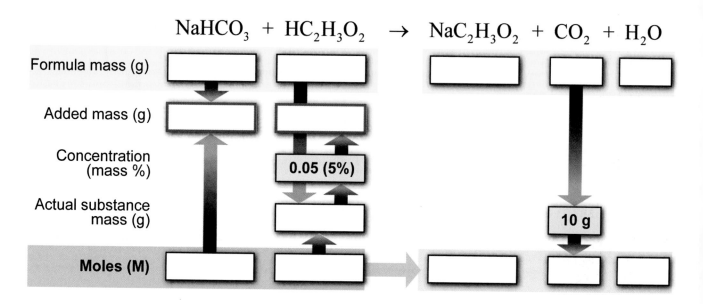

$$NaHCO_3 + HC_2H_3O_2 \rightarrow NaC_2H_3O_2 + CO_2 + H_2O$$

Formula mass (g)

Added mass (g)

Concentration (mass %)   0.05 (5%)

Actual substance mass (g)   10 g

Moles (M)

a. Calculate the number of moles in 10 g of CO_2.

b. How many moles of acetic acid and sodium bicarbonate are needed to produce this many moles of CO_2?

c. Use the formula mass to calculate the mass of acetic acid in grams.

d. Divide the mass of acetic acid by 0.05 to get the mass of vinegar you need (red box, second column).

e. Use the formula mass to calculate the mass of baking soda you need (red box, first column).

Part 8: Applying the principle

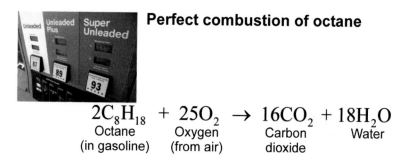

Perfect combustion of octane

We use gasoline in cars, trucks, and buses. The reaction in a gasoline engine combines octane and other hydrocarbon molecules with oxygen in the air. If the fuel is burned perfectly, only water and carbon dioxide are produced as products.

$$2C_8H_{18} + 25O_2 \rightarrow 16CO_2 + 18H_2O$$

Octane (in gasoline)   Oxygen (from air)   Carbon dioxide   Water

a. Calculate the formula mass for octane.

b. Suppose a car uses 25 gallons of gasoline in a week. The density of gasoline is about 2,900 g/gallon. Calculate the mass in grams of 25 gallons of gasoline.

c. For simplicity's sake, assume gasoline is pure octane (which it isn't). How many moles does this quantity represent?

d. How many moles of CO_2 are created for every 2 moles of gasoline burned?

e. Calculate the mass of CO_2 released from the perfect combustion of 25 gallons of gasoline.

86

A NATURAL APPROACH TO
CHEMISTRY

11B: Stoichiometry: Quantitative Precipitate

Do the principles of stoichiometry really work? How do you use stoichiometry to determine the percentage yield of a reaction?

This experiment will give us the opportunity to see if stoichiometry can actually predict the amount of products formed from a certain amount of reactants. By carrying out a precipitation reaction that forms solid copper(II) carbonate, we can measure the amount of product produced. This will be our "actual" yield. We can then compare the amount of product obtained to the calculated or "theoretical" yield based on stoichiometry. We will also use the data to determine the percentage yield of the solid product copper(II) carbonate.

Materials

- Two 250 mL Erlenmeyer flasks or beakers
- Two stirring rods
- One medium funnel
- One piece of fast-flow filter paper
- Distilled water bottle
- Copper(II) chloride ($CuCl_2$)
- Sodium carbonate (Na_2CO_3)
- Mass balance

This lab uses a *double replacement* or *precipitate* reaction between copper(II) chloride ($CuCl_2$) and sodium carbonate (Na_2CO_3). We will be able to predict the amount of product that should be formed according to the reaction:

$$CuCl_2(aq) + Na_2CO_3(aq) \rightarrow CuCO_3(s) + 2NaCl(aq)$$

from the masses of reactants used. Before you begin, read through the entire procedure below so that you are familiar with each of the necessary steps.

Part 1: Preparing the solutions

Table 1. Data table for Part 1

	Mass (g)	Observations
$CuCl_2(s)$		
$Na_2CO_3(s)$		
Filter paper		
Mass of $CuCO_3(s)$ and filter paper		
Mass of $CuCO_3(s)$		

1. You will need two clean 250 mL beakers or Erlenmeyer flasks.

2. Measure out approximately 1 g each of $CuCl_2$ and Na_2CO_3 solids. The actual amount can be between 0.9 g and 1.1 g; it does not have to be exactly one. Record the exact amount that you measured in your data table.

3. Place each solid in a beaker and add 25–30 mL of distilled water. Gently stir the mixture to dissolve the salts. Be sure to use a *different* stirring rod for each, so that you do not cross–contaminate your solutions.

4. Record the color of each of your solutions.

Part 2: The precipitate reaction

1. Slowly add a little $CuCl_2$ solution to the Na_2CO_3. Swirl to mix and record your observations.

2. Slowly continue to add the $CuCl_2$ to the Na_2CO_3 and swirl to mix. The slow addition of $CuCl_2$ along with continuous swirling allows for the greatest amount of product to be formed, because more ions are able to contact each other.

3. When all of the solution is added, rinse the empty flask with 3–5 mL of distilled water and add this to the mixture. This removes any remaining $CuCl_2$ ions.

Part 3: Isolating the product

1. Obtain a piece of filter paper and fold it according to your instructor's demonstration. (Fold it in half and then in half again.) Write your name in pencil near the top outside edge of the filter paper.

2. Weigh the filter paper.

3. Place the filter paper in the funnel, and place the funnel inside the neck of an empty Erlenmeyer flask. To make the funnel more secure, it helps to use a ring stand and place the funnel inside the ring with the flask below it.

4. Wet the filter paper with a little distilled water so that three folds of paper are on one side and one paper thickness is on the other. This helps it stick to the funnel and keeps it in place.

5. Swirl your mixture to suspend the solid in the solution. Slowly pour the mixture into the filter paper. As you pour the mixture, be sure that the solution does not come above the filter paper. Check to see that the "filtrate" (the solution draining into the flask below the funnel) is clear. If it is not clear, you may have a tear in your filter paper, or some mixture may have escaped over the top. You will need to refilter this to ensure that you capture all of your solid.

6. Remove your filter paper containing the $CuCO_3$ solid and place it in the area designated by your instructor, where it will dry overnight.

7. Clean and rinse all equipment. You may need to use a test tube brush to remove solid particles stuck to the sides of glassware.

8. During the next class period, weigh your filter paper and solid. Record the color and mass of the $CuCO_3$ in your data table.

Part 4: Determining the percentage yield of your reaction

1. Write out the balanced equation for this reaction.
2. Complete the data table below.

Table 2. Data table for Part 4

	Mass (g)	Molar mass (g/mole)	Moles
CuCl$_2$(s)			
Na$_2$CO$_3$(s)			
CuCO$_3$(s) (actual yield)			
Limiting reactant			
Theoretical yield of CuCO$_3$(s)			

3. Calculate your percentage yield of $CuCO_3$ in this reaction.
4. Was your percentage yield 100%? If not, give some reasons that you think may have caused this difference.
5. List two sources of error that could have caused your actual yield to be low.
6. List one source of error that could have caused your actual yield to be falsely high. Explain.

Part 5: What did you learn?

a. Describe what you learned about precipitate reactions from this investigation in a couple of sentences.

b. Write a couple of sentences that explain how the actual yield and theoretical yield of $CuCO_3$ compare for your experiment.

c. Compare your results with those of another group. How do your results compare?

d. What do you think was the largest source of error in obtaining a high percentage yield? Explain.

e. In this experiment, what is the mole relationship between your reactants and the product $CuCO_3$?

f. Did the limiting reactant need to be calculated in this investigation, given the fact that you used almost the same amounts of reactants? Briefly explain your answer.

g. If you could do this experiment again, what would you do differently that might improve your percentage yield of $CuCO_3$?

Part 6: Practicing what you learned

Suppose you carry out another similar experiment, this time with a different precipitate according to the following equation:

$$2NaOH(aq) + CuSO_4(aq) \rightarrow Cu(OH)_2(s) + Na_2SO_4(aq)$$

In this experiment you obtain the following data:

Table 3. Data table for Part 6

	Mass (g)	Molar mass (g/mole)	Moles
$CuCl_2(s)$	1.0		
NaOH(s)	1.8		
$Cu(OH)_2(s)$ actual yield			
Limiting reactant			
Theoretical yield of $Cu(OH)_2(s)$			

a. Calculate the molar mass of your reactants and solid product [$Cu(OH)_2$], and list them in the table above.

b. Calculate the moles of your reactants and solid product [$Cu(OH)_2$], and list them in the table above.

c. Determine which reactant was limiting. Support your answer with a calculation.

d. Using your limiting reactant, determine how much solid $Cu(OH)_2$ you could have made if all of your reactants reacted and you were able to collect 100% of your solid product. What is this called?

e. Determine the percentage yield for this reaction. Support your answer with a calculation.

f. Give at least one source of error that could account for your result. Explain.

12A: Respiration and Temperature

Why are living organisms dependent on temperature?

Almost all chemical reactions are affected by temperature. This is because temperature supplies some or all of the activation energy needed by chemical reactions. Higher temperature means more molecules have sufficient energy to react. Temperature sensitivity is very strong in living systems. Most plants and animals can only thrive within a narrow range of temperatures. This investigation will look at how the chemical processes of life are affected by temperature.

Materials	
• Lab-Master with temperature probe and heater	• Balance (0.1 g)
	• 5–10 g rapid-rise yeast
• 25 mm test tube	• 5–10 g sugar
• Two hole stopper with 7 mm glass tube inserted in one hole (premade)	• Stopwatch
	• Centimeter ruler
	• Weighing papers
	• Permanent marker

Part 1: Cellular respiration

Respiration is exothermic

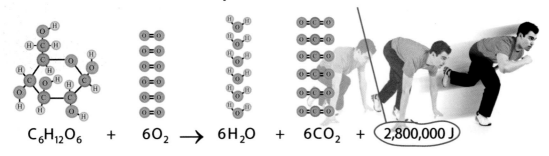

$$C_6H_{12}O_6 \ + \ 6O_2 \longrightarrow 6H_2O \ + \ 6CO_2 \ + \ 2{,}800{,}000 \ J$$

Living organisms eat food to get energy from their environment. At the microscopic level, the process of extracting energy from food is called *cellular respiration*. The actual chemical reactions proceed in many steps, but the overall reaction is to convert glucose and oxygen into carbon dioxide, water, and energy. The energy is stored in a rechargeable molecular "battery" called adenosine triphosphate (ATP).

In this investigation, we will see how the reactions of cellular respiration are affected by temperature. The results will tell us a great deal about why Earth is so well suited for life.

Part 2: Questions to think about

a. What is the maximum temperature at which living things can survive?

b. What is the minimum temperature at which living things can survive?

c. What is the average temperature of your body in degrees Celsius and in degrees Fahrenheit?

d. What is the average temperature of Earth's surface in degrees Celsius and in degrees Fahrenheit?

e. What are the approximate high and low temperatures in areas where people live (in degrees Celsius and in degrees Fahrenheit)?

Part 3: Setting up

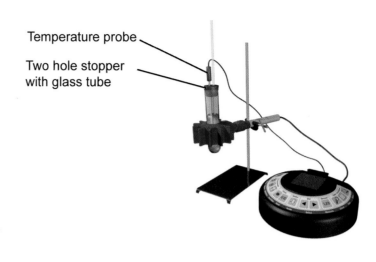

Temperature probe

Two hole stopper
with glass tube

1. Set up the Lab-Master with the temperature probe and the heater.

2. Put 20 mL of water in the test tube and bring it to the temperature you are assigned by your instructor.

3. While the water is heating up, measure out 1 g of sugar and 1 g of yeast.

4. Record the temperature of water on a table similar to Table 1 on the next page.

5. Take the test tube out of the heater and add the sugar. Stir well and put the test tube back in the heater.

6. Take the stopper with the glass tube and make two marks 10 cm apart with a permanent marker. The lowest mark needs to be at least 5 cm from the stopper. The glass tubing should be about 1 cm from the bottom of the test tube.

7. Insert the temperature probe in the other hole so it sticks down at least 1 cm into the water.

Part 4: How the experiment works

When you add the yeast to the sugar water, the microscopic yeast will start to live and grow. This means the yeast will "eat" the sugar and produce carbon dioxide gas. If the stopper is snug in the test tube, the CO_2 gas will make the pressure in the test tube go up. In turn, this will force water up the glass tube.

The *rate* of chemical reactions within the yeast directly affects how fast the water rises up the tube. By measuring how long it takes for the water to rise 10 cm, you can measure the rate of cellular respiration of the yeast. Of course, as the yeast grow and multiply, this reaction rate will change. To make everyone's data consistent, each group will wait exactly 3 minutes after adding the yeast to make a measurement. Leave the stopper open while waiting.

You only get one chance to make a measurement once you have added the yeast. It is important to be ready. Practice what you are going to do before starting the experiment.

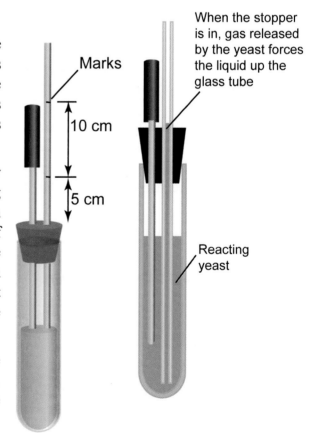

When the stopper is in, gas released by the yeast forces the liquid up the glass tube

Marks

10 cm

5 cm

Reacting yeast

When the yeast mixture has reached the higher mark, quickly loosen the stopper in the test tube and release the pressure. Otherwise the yeast mixture will overflow the top of the tube.

Part 5: The experiment

Investigating sugar content on reaction rate

1. Make sure you have everything ready: The temperature probe is at the right height in the stopper, the water is at temperature, the sugar is mixed, the stopwatch is ready, and your marks are on the glass tube.

2. Remove the test tube and carefully stir in the yeast. Place the test tube back in the heater, with the stopper resting on top of the test tube, but not pushed in, so that the temperature probe is in contact with the solution.

3. After 3 minutes, put the stopper in the test tube to form a seal. Measure how long it takes the water to get from the first mark to the second mark (10 cm higher). Record your data in Table 1.

0.5 g sugar	1.0 g sugar	2.0 g sugar
1 g yeast	1 g yeast	1 g yeast
20 mL water	20 mL water	20 mL water

4. Release the pressure by lifting the stopper and resting it on the edge of the test tube.

5. Repeat the procedure (Steps 1–3) using 0.5 g of sugar.

6. Repeat the procedure (Steps 1–3) using 2.0 g of sugar.

Table 1. Respiration reaction data

Sugar (g)	Temperature (°C)	Time to rise 10 cm (s)	Rate of rise (mm/s)
0.5			
1.0			
2.0			

Part 6: Thinking about what you observed

a. Calculate the speed in millimeters per second at which the liquid rises (rate of rise) and record it in Table 1. This is 100 mm divided by the time it takes. This speed is a direct measure of the reaction rate.

Table 2. Class data for respiration reaction

Temperature (°C)	Rate of rise (mm/s)		
	0.5 g sugar	1.0 g sugar	2.0 g sugar

b. Each group will repeat the experiment for several different temperatures. Collect the data from the class and organize them like the format of Table 2. Make a graph of rate of rise versus temperature. The graph should have temperature on the x axis. The rate of rise in millimeters per second should be on the y axis since this is a measure of the reaction rate. Draw a separate plot for each sugar amount.

c. What does the graph look like? Is it a straight line? Is it a curve? Does it have a hump?

d. At what temperature does the reaction go fastest?

e. What does this experiment tell you about the temperature range that yeast find most suitable for life?

Part 7: Investigating other aspects of the environment

There are other chemical variables that affect the ability of living organisms to thrive and grow. One of the most important ones is pH, and another is the presence of environmental factors such as salt and other compounds.

a. Design an experiment to test the impact of pH on respiration. Carry out the experiment and state your conclusion.

b. Design an experiment to test the effect of salt concentration on respiration in yeast. Carry out the experiment and state your conclusion.

For each of the experiments, you should do the following:

1. Create a data table and record data that you can use to evaluate your research question.
2. Analyze the data, using appropriate techniques such as graphing and error analysis.
3. Write down a formal hypothesis for your experiment.
4. Write down a brief procedure for your experiment.
5. Write down a paragraph for a conclusion.

12B: Reaction Rate and Concentration

How does a change in reactant concentration affect the reaction rate?

The study of reaction rates is related to a topic in chemistry referred to as kinetics. In this investigation, solid sulfur is produced as a product of a decomposition reaction. You will time how long sulfur takes to form an opaque yellow colloidal suspension. By adding different amounts of reactants, you will be able to observe how the reaction rate changes. The speed of a chemical reaction depends upon several factors. Here we will investigate what effect changing the concentration of reactants has on the formation of solid sulfur.

Materials

- Six 50 mL beakers or Erlenmeyer flasks
- Filter paper marked with a black **X**
- Lab-Master for timing
- One 10 mL graduated cylinder
- One 50 mL graduated cylinder
- Distilled water bottle
- 5 mL pipets (optional), two cuvettes (optional)
- 100 mL of 1.0 M HCl
- 200 mL of 1.0 M $Na_2S_2O_3$ solution
- Glass stirring rod
- Rubber gloves (disposable)

In this experiment we use a solution of sodium thiosulfate [$Na_2S_2O_3(aq)$]. You are familiar with sodium, but probably not the thiosulfate ion. The thiosulfate ion ($S_2O_3^{2-}$) is another polyatomic ion similar to carbonate (CO_3^{2-}). We are introducing this new ion because it is useful in learning about reaction speeds. Aqueous solutions containing the thiosulfate ion ($S_2O_3^{2-}$) decompose quickly when acid is added to them. The decomposition follows the following reaction:

$$S_2O_3^{2-} + 2H^+ \rightarrow \underset{\substack{\text{yellow} \\ \text{color}}}{S(s)} + SO_2(g) + H_2O$$

This reaction is very useful because it produces a yellow suspension of sulfur (S) that we can see with our eyes and measure with the spectrophotometer. Because sulfur is insoluble in aqueous solutions, the solution will first begin to look cloudy and then become opaque.

During our experiments, we will place the beaker or Erlenmeyer flask on top of a piece of filter paper marked with a black **X**. Once the reaction starts we will time how long it takes for the **X** mark to no longer be visible. The SO_2 gas produced is very soluble in water, so interestingly no bubbles are seen during the reaction.

Part 1: Making a hypothesis

Before we begin, consider how a change in reactant concentration may affect the rate of our chemical reaction. Use your background knowledge of reaction rates from your text to help you here.

a. Make a hypothesis that states how increasing the concentration of one or both reactant(s) will affect the rate of the reaction we are carrying out.

b. Make a second hypothesis that states how decreasing the concentration of one or both reactant(s) will affect the rate of the reaction.

Part 2: Varying thiosulfate concentration

1. *Safety note*: Do not breathe the acid fumes directly. Immediately notify your instructor of a spill. You may sprinkle baking soda on any spill to neutralize the acid.

2. For each trial listed in the Table 1 below, measure the indicated volume of thiosulfate solution and water into a 50 mL beaker and stir well. Be sure to label the numbers on your beakers so they do not get mixed up. When measuring, you may wish to use an eye dropper to help adjust the meniscus and to obtain more accurate results.

3. Place the first beaker on the filter paper marked with a black **X**. Pour in the 25.0 mL of 1.0 M HCl and swirl gently to mix. Start timing the instant the acid is added. Stop timing when the **X** is no longer visible. This is your reaction time. It is helpful to have the same person time each reaction so that the endpoint is determined consistently throughout the trials. The endpoint determination is somewhat subjective, but the results will be good as long as measurement is careful. You may need to practice the timing once for practice. If for some reason something goes wrong with a trial, you can always repeat it. Record the time in Table 1.

4. (Optional) When you are finished timing, immediately place the solution in a cuvette and measure the RGB absorbance in the spectrophotometer. Remember to calibrate the spectrophotometer with distilled water before your first measurement.

5. Calculate the concentration of thiosulfate ion ($S_2O_3^{2-}$) and record it in Table 1.

6. Repeat Steps 3 and 4 for each of your five concentrations of thiosulfate.

Table 1. Effect of thiosulfate concentration

Trial	Volume of thiosulfate (mL)	Volume of water (mL)	Volume of acid (mL)	Time (s)	$[S_2O_3^{2-}]$ (M)
1	5	0	25		
2	4	1	25		
3	3	2	25		
4	2	3	25		
5	1	4	25		

Part 3: Varying acid concentration

In this section, we will repeat a similar procedure by following the amounts in Table 2 below.

1. For each trial (6–10) listed in Table 2, measure 5.0 mL of thiosulfate solution into a 50 mL beaker. Be sure to label your beaker.

2. Place the beaker on the filter paper marked with a black **X**.

3. Mix the acid and water together in a small graduated cylinder. Together they should add up to a total volume of 25.0 mL.

4. Add the acid–water mixture to the thiosulfate solution and swirl gently. Again, start timing the instant the acid and water mixture are mixed. Stop timing when the **X** is no longer visible. Once again it is helpful to have the same person time each trial. Record the time in Table 2.

5. (Optional) When you are finished timing, immediately place the solution in a cuvette and measure the RGB absorbance in the spectrophotometer. Remember to calibrate the spectrophotometer with distilled water before your first measurement.

6. Calculate the concentration of hydrogen ions (H^+) and record it in Table 2.

7. Repeat Steps 2–6 for each of your five concentrations of acid.

Table 2. Effect of acid concentration

Trial	Volume of thiosulfate (mL)	Volume of water (mL)	Volume of acid (mL)	Time (s)	$[H^+]$ (M)
6	5	0	25		
7	5	5	20		
8	5	10	15		
9	5	15	10		
10	5	20	5		

Part 4: Thinking about it

a. Trials 1 and 6 are the same, so compare your results. Are they similar?

b. Explain why it is helpful to have the same person time each trial.

c. What was different about the trials done in Parts 2 and 3?

d. Briefly explain why the **X** disappeared after mixing the solutions.

e. What did you notice about the time it took for the **X** to disappear? Explain.

Part 5: Making graphs

a. Make your graphs on the computer using a spreadsheet program. Give your graph a title and label the axes with appropriate units. Select a line graph for the graph type.

b. Make a graph of time versus the concentration of thiosulfate ($S_2O_3{}^{2-}$).

c. Make a second graph of time versus the concentration of acid (H^+).

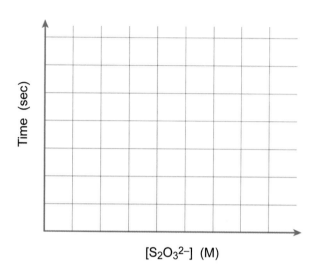
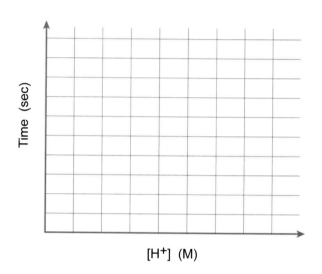

Part 6: What did you learn?

a. Look carefully at each of your graphs. Write a couple of sentences explaining how they are different.

b. Did you notice a change in the reaction time when you varied the acid concentration? Be sure to use your graphs to help explain your answer.

c. Did you notice a change in the reaction time when you varied the thiosulfate concentration? Be sure to use your graphs to help explain your answer.

d. Which trial gave you more of a noticeable change?

e. Why should increasing the concentration of a reactant increase the rate of the reaction? Explain.

f. Were your hypotheses correct? Explain.

g. Do you think that it is possible that one reactant might affect the reaction rate more than the other?

h. What are two other factors that also affect the rate of a chemical reaction?

i. In your opinion, what was the largest source of error in this experiment? Explain why.

j. List two additional sources of *experimental* error that may have been a factor in your results.

k. (Optional) Using your data from Part 2, graph the rate as 1/time on the *y* axis and the thiosulfate concentration on the *x* axis. If you get a linear relationship, you will be able to prove the reaction is first order with respect to the thiosulfate concentration.

12C: Le Châtelier's Principle

How do chemical systems react to change? Does Le Châtelier's principle really predict the behavior of a chemical system?

During this investigation you will observe the equilibrium of a complex ion ($FeSCN^{2+}$). Aqueous solutions of iron(III) (Fe^{3+}) and thiocyanate ions (SCN^-) are mixed to form $FeSCN^{2+}$. While adding different chemicals to this system, you will be able to see *Le Châtelier's Principle* in action. Le Châtelier's principle states that a system in equilibrium will shift to partially relieve a stress or change placed on the system. As always, your observations are the key to your obtaining good results. Recall that spectator ions are not involved in the formation of products; they remain unchanged during the reaction.

Materials
• Ten 12 mm, 10 mL test tubes
• Test tube rack
• One dropper bottle (25 mL) of 0.002 M $Fe(NO_3)_3$
• One dropper bottle of 0.002 M KSCN
• One dropper bottle of 1.0 M KSCN
• One dropper bottle of 1.0 M $Fe(NO_3)_3$
• One dropper bottle of 6.0 M KOH
• Solid K_3PO_4
• Beaker of crushed ice
• Distilled water bottle
• Lab-Master with heater and 25 mm test tube

In this investigation, it is helpful to know that 2.0 mL is about 2.0 cm high on these 10 mL test tubes. You can use this as a guideline so that you do *not* need to measure 2.0 mL in a graduated cylinder for each part of the experiment.

*Important Note: There are two different concentrations of $Fe(NO_3)_3$ and KSCN. Be sure to use the correct one.

$$Fe^{3+}(aq) \quad + \quad SCN^-(aq) \quad \rightleftarrows \quad FeSCN^{2+}(aq)$$

clear   clear   red/orange
light yellow

**Note that since NO^{3-} and K^+ are spectator ions, they are not involved in the reaction
and are not shown in the equation**

Part 1: Setting up

1. In a small test tube, add 2 mL of 0.002 M ferric nitrate [$Fe(NO_3)_3$] and 2 mL of 0.002 M potassium thiocyanate (KSCN). Use an empty test tube to mix the contents back and forth. Describe the color change and keep this test tube as your control. The control is used to do comparison checks against other test tubes.

2. Prepare seven additional identical test tubes, each containing 2 mL of 0.002 M ferric nitrate [$Fe(NO_3)_3$] and 2 mL of 0.002 M potassium thiocyanate (KSCN). Mix each one and compare. You should note that they all look similar in color. If one looks different, discard it and prepare it again.

Part 2: Observations

In each step below you will create a change that causes the equilibrium of the complex ion ($FeSCN^{2+}$) to shift to the left or to the right. You can tell which way it shifts by looking at the color change and the equation on the previous page. For example, if you see that the color shifts from red to yellow, the reaction goes from right to left. If the color shifts from yellow to red the reaction proceeds from left to right. Be sure to make only one change per test tube.

1. Add 2–3 drops of 1.0 M KSCN, a source of K^+ and SCN^-. Mix by pouring back and forth in another clean test tube. Record your observations.

2. Add a few drops of 1 M $Fe(NO_3)_3$, a source of Fe^{3+} and NO_3^-. Mix and record your observations.

3. Add a few drops of 6 M KOH, a source of K^+ and OH^-. Mix and record your observations.

4. Add a few tiny pieces of solid K_3PO_4, a source of K^+ and PO_4^{3-}. Mix and record your observations.

5. Add 5.0 mL of distilled water. Mix and record your observations.

6. Place the reaction on ice for 2–3 minutes. Observe what happens relative to your control test tube.

7. Place the reaction in some hot water for 2–3 minutes. Either use hot tap water or heat a test tube of water using the Lab-Master heater. Observe what happens to the reaction mixture relative to your control test tube.

8. Compare the ice and hot water test tubes next to each other. Record your observations.

Part 3: Thinking about it

1. How can you determine whether or not a change occurred in your equilibrium mixture? Explain.

2. For each reaction in Part 2, explain how each change can be described by Le Châtelier's principle. To do this, look at the chemical reaction shown on page 99. Note the colors of the ions on the reactant side and the color of the product. Be specific about what chemical was added that is part of your equilibrium system. Disregard spectator ions. Was your color change lighter or darker? If it was darker, then the change caused the equilibrium to shift to the products side. If it became lighter than your control, the equilibrium shifted to the reactants side.

3. Use your observations from Steps 3 and 4 of Part 2 to explain why your system became lighter or darker. Here you will need to refer back to your solubility rules and think about how a precipitate would affect your concentration of ions.

4. Use your observations from Steps 6 and 7 of Part 2 to explain whether this equilibrium reaction is exothermic or endothermic in the forward direction.

Part 4: What did you learn?

1. Did this experiment help you to understand Le Châtelier's principle? Why or why not?

2. Was the control test tube helpful?

3. Complex ions such as ferric thiocyanate often form brilliantly colored solutions. See whether you can find another complex ion using the Internet. Write down its chemical formula and its color.

A NATURAL APPROACH TO
CHEMISTRY

13A: The pH Scale

What does pH actually measure?

The pH scale is associated with acids and bases. It is a logarithmic scale, meaning a change of 1 pH unit means the concentration of H^+ ions in solution changes by a factor of 10. In this investigation, you will measure pH indirectly using indicators and absorption using the Lab-Master.

Materials

- Six cuvettes
- Two 100 mL graduated cylinders
- Six 12 mm test tubes
- Test tube rack
- Lab-Master
- Universal indicator solution
- Methyl orange
- 1 M HCl
- 1 M NaOH

Part 1: Setting up for acids

1. Label six small test tubes with numbers 1 through 6 and place them in your test tube rack.

2. Make mixture #1 by adding 5 mL of 1 M HCl to 45 mL of distilled water. *Mix* well by pouring back and forth.

3. Put about 10 mL of mixture #1 in test tube #1 and save it for later.

4. Make mixture #2 by adding 5 mL of mixture #1 to 45 mL of water. Mix well.

5. Put 10 mL of mixture #2 in test tube #2 and save it for later.

6. Clean out the first graduated cylinder. Make mixture #3 by adding 5 mL of mixture #2 to 45 mL of water. Mix well.

7. Save 10 mL of mixture #3 in test tube #3 and save it for later.

8. Repeat the process three more times, each time mixing 5 mL of each mixture with 45 mL of water to get the next mixture. Be sure each of your solutions are well mixed. You should finish with six test tubes like the diagram below.

Mixture #1

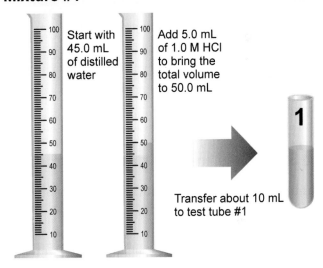

Start with 45.0 mL of distilled water

Add 5.0 mL of 1.0 M HCl to bring the total volume to 50.0 mL

Transfer about 10 mL to test tube #1

Mixture #2

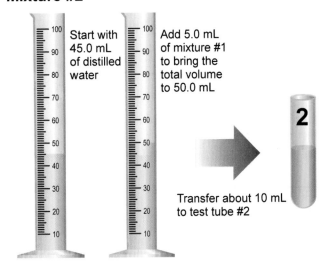

Start with 45.0 mL of distilled water

Add 5.0 mL of mixture #1 to bring the total volume to 50.0 mL

Transfer about 10 mL to test tube #2

Part 2: Doing the math for acids

Each of the test tubes has a different concentration of acid. In this next step, you are going to calculate the concentration of each one.

a. First calculate the volume of acid in each mixture using the concentration of the previous mixture.

b. Use the result of (a) to calculate the concentration of the mixture itself. Record your calculations in a table similar to Table 1.

> **Definition of pH**
>
> $$pH = -\log[H^+]$$
>
> pH is -1 times the logarithm of the H^+ molarity

Table 1. Concentration data for acid measurement

Test tube #	Volume of 1 M HCl (mL)	Total Volume (mL)	Moles H^+	H^+ molarity	pH
1	5	50	0.005	0.1	1.0
2	0.5	50			
3		50			
4		50			
5		50			
6		50			

Part 3: Measuring the color for acids

Set up six cuvettes then add 1 drop of methyl orange to each

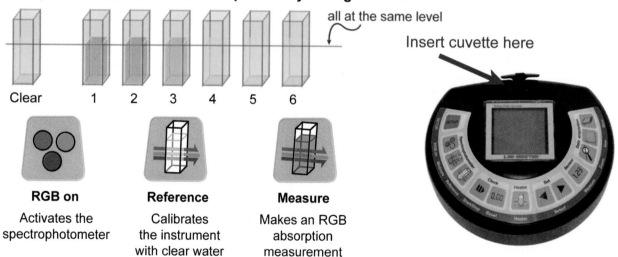

Clear   1   2   3   4   5   6

all at the same level

Insert cuvette here

RGB on
Activates the spectrophotometer

Reference
Calibrates the instrument with clear water

Measure
Makes an RGB absorption measurement

For many scientific experiments, the human eye is not reliable enough to make an objective measurement. For the next part of the experiment you are going to use the spectrophotometer to measure the pH.

1. Calibrate the spectrophotometer using a cuvette with 2 mL of distilled water

2. Put about 2 mL of each solution into separate cuvettes. Add 1 drop of methyl orange to each cuvette. Be careful to add *only* 1 drop.

3. Take an RGB reading from each cuvette. Record the RGB measurements in a table similar to Table 2 shown on the next page, and transfer the pH values from Table 1 to this new table.

Table 2. Spectrophotometer data for acid concentrations

Test tube #	pH	R (AU)	G (AU)	B (AU)
1	1.0			
2				
3				
4				
5				
6				

Part 4: Observations

a. What can you say about the appearance of the cuvettes? How do they compare to each other? Which is the lightest? Which is the darkest? Do any appear the same? Give an answer in two or three sentences.

b. Do your observations agree with what you expected?

Part 5: Thinking about what you observed

a. Plot graphs of R, G, and B versus pH on the same graph axis. (Use graph paper similar to the one shown on page 105.)

b. Which of the colors was most sensitive to this range of pH?

c. Are there any pH ranges for which this technique would not work?

Part 6: Setting up for bases

Clean your acid cuvettes and test tubes well. You will need them to prepare a pH series of bases next.

1. Label six small test tubes with numbers 8 through 13.
2. Make mixture #13 by adding 5 mL of 1 M NaOH to 45 mL of distilled water. Put about 30 mL of this solution into test tube #13 and save it for later measurements.
3. Make mixture #12 by adding 5 mL of mixture #13 to 45 mL of water. Put about 30 mL into test tube #12 and save it for later measurements.
4. Clean out the first graduated cylinder. Make mixture #11 by adding 5 mL of mixture #12 to 45 mL of water. Save 30 mL of this solution in test tube #11.
5. Repeat the process three more times, each time mixing 5 mL of each mixture with 45 mL of water to get the next mixture. You should finish with six test tubes.

Part 7: Doing the math for bases

Each of the test tubes has a different concentration of base. In this next step, you are going to calculate the concentration of base in each one.

a.   First calculate the volume of base in each mixture using the concentration of the previous mixture.

b.   Use the result of (a) to calculate the concentration of the mixture itself. Record your calculations in a table similar to Table 3.

> **Definition of pH**
>
> $$pH = 14 + \log[OH^-]$$
>
> pH is proportional to the logarithm of the OH⁻ molarity

Table 3. Concentration data for base measurement

Test tube #	Volume of 1 M NaOH (mL)	Total volume (mL)	Moles OH⁻	OH⁻ molarity	pH
13	5	50	0.005	0.1	13.0
12	0.5	50			
11		50			
10		50			
9		50			
8		50			

Part 8: Measuring the color for bases

Here we follow the same procedure as in Part 3, but using a universal indicator. Record the data in Table 4.

Set up six cuvettes then add 1 drop of universal indicator to each

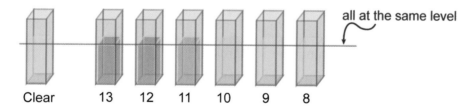

all at the same level

Clear   13   12   11   10   9   8

Table 4. Spectrophotometer data for base concentrations

Test tube #	pH	R (AU)	G (AU)	B (AU)
13	13.0			
12				
11				
10				
9				
8				

a.   Now using the base paper, plot graphs of R, G, and B versus pH. (Use graph paper similar to the one shown on page 106.)

b.   Which of the colors was most sensitive to this range of pH using the universal indicator solution?

RGB Calibration vs. pH for acids

Indicator _____

Amount per cuvette _____

A NATURAL APPROACH TO
CHEMISTRY

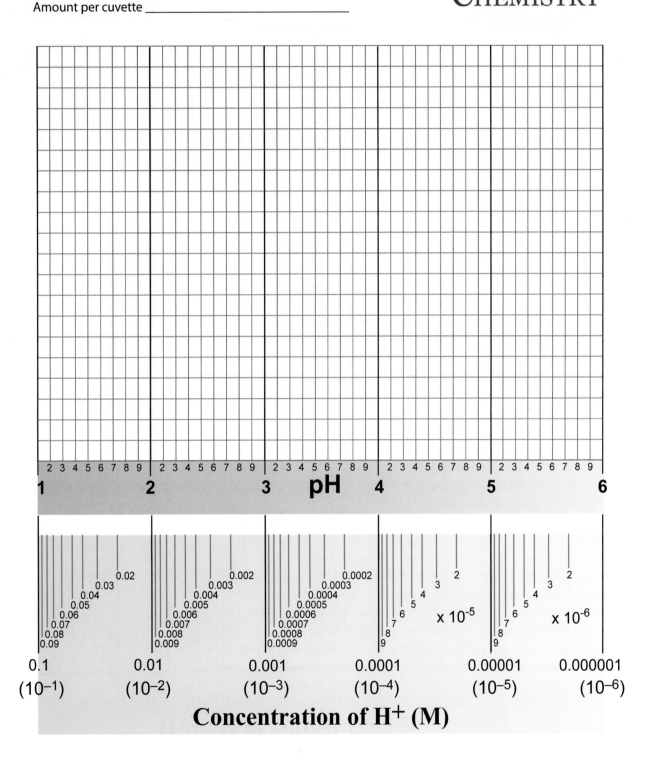

Absorbance

pH

1   2   3   4   5   6

0.02
0.03
0.04
0.05
0.06
0.07
0.08
0.09

0.002
0.003
0.004
0.005
0.006
0.007
0.008
0.009

0.0002
0.0003
0.0004
0.0005
0.0006
0.0007
0.0008
0.0009

2
3
4
5
6
7
8
9
$\times 10^{-5}$

2
3
4
5
6
7
8
9
$\times 10^{-6}$

0.1
(10^{-1})

0.01
(10^{-2})

0.001
(10^{-3})

0.0001
(10^{-4})

0.00001
(10^{-5})

0.000001
(10^{-6})

Concentration of H$^+$ (M)

RGB Calibration vs. pH for bases

Indicator _____

Amount per cuvette _____

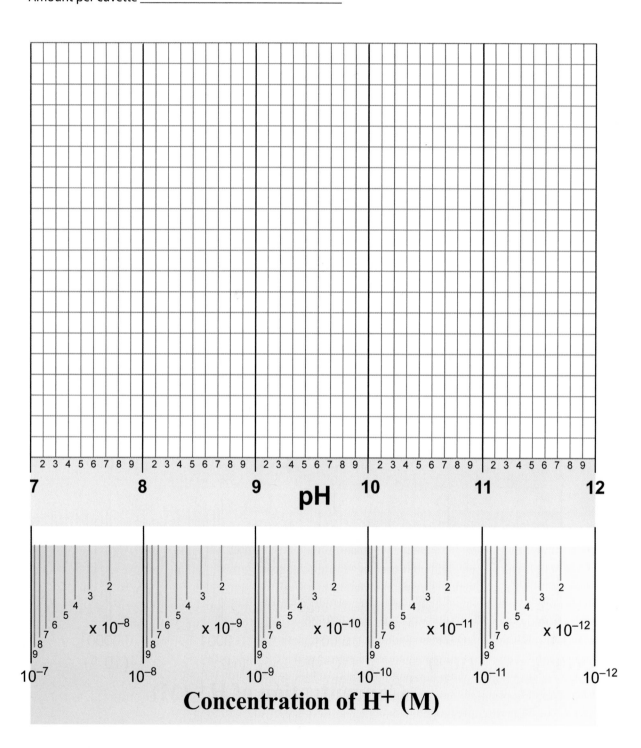

13B: Titration of Vinegar

How can we determine how much acetic acid is in vinegar?
How accurate is the advertised amount of acetic acid in vinegar?

The acetic acid in vinegar comes from the apples or grapes used to make it. Commercial vinegar contains mostly water, and it is advertised as approximately 5% acetic acid by mass. In this investigation we will titrate vinegar with standardized NaOH. *Titration* is a process used to determine the moles of an acid or base in an aqueous solution. We will slowly add drops of NaOH to the vinegar, and our solution will change color when the ratio of acid to base is close to the same. To form water, we need equal amounts of acid and base. Titrations use indicators to signal when the endpoint is near.

Materials
• Vinegar (normal strength)
• Erlenmeyer flask
• Distilled water
• Phenolphthalein indicator
• 50 mL graduated cylinder
• 10 mL graduated cylinder
• Beral pipet
• Dropper bottle of 1.0 M NaOH
• Mass balance

The acid–base reaction carried out in this experiment is

$$CH_3COOH(aq) + NaOH(aq) \rightarrow H_2O(l) + NaCH_3COO(aq)$$

Our goal is to completely "neutralize" the acetic acid (CH_3COOH). If we add just the right amount of NaOH to the solution, we will end up with water (H_2O) and salt ($NaCH_3COO$, sodium acetate). When the solution is neutral, we can say that the endpoint has been reached.

At the endpoint, the moles of acid are equal to the moles of base. This is the most important aspect of the titration process.

Part 1: Titration procedure

1. Weigh a clean, dry 125 mL Erlenmeyer flask.

2. Measure 1.6 mL of vinegar in your small graduated cylinder, and add it to the Erlenmeyer flask

3. Weigh the flask and the vinegar so that you can calculate the exact mass of vinegar you are titrating.

4. Add approximately 25 mL of distilled water to the flask. Swirl to mix.

5. Add 3–4 drops of phenolphthalein indicator to the vinegar. Swirl to mix.

6. Using your beral pipet, calibrate the number of drops in one milliliter. You may have done this before by counting how many drops it takes to reach the 1.0 mL mark on your graduated cylinder. This is very important. It allows you to estimate the volume you use to titrate. Once you know how many drops are in one milliliter, you can begin.

7. Add drops of NaOH slowly to your Erlenmeyer flask. Swirl to mix after every few drops.

8. You are looking for a pink color that persists throughout the solution for 30 to 60 s. To accomplish this, you must swirl often and add your drops slowly. One drop can cause you to go too far. If your solution is too pink and does not go away, this means you have gone too far past your "endpoint" and your solution is not basic. You actually want your solution to be neutral.

9. Repeat Steps 1–8 three times to obtain a reliable and (hopefully) reproducible result.

10. Rinse your titration down the sink with water and clean your glassware.

Part 2: Thinking about it

1. What does the pink color tell you about your titration?

2. How can you determine the volume of the base you used? Explain.

Part 3: Calculations

1. Enter your data in Table 1. For comparison, gather some other data from other groups.

Table 1. Class data

Mass of vinegar (g)	Volume of NaOH (mL)	Moles of NaOH	Moles of acetic acid	Percent by mass of acetic acid

2. Determine the number of moles of NaOH you used to titrate your vinegar using the molarity formula. $M = X$ moles / (your volume in liters).

3. The mole ratio is one to one based on the chemical reaction. Knowing the moles of NaOH allows you to find the moles of acetic acid.

4. Next, convert your moles of acetic acid to grams of acetic acid (CH_3COOH) using the molar mass. Show your calculations and enter your results on Table 1.

5. Lastly, determine your percent by mass of acetic acid:

6. Record your value in Table 1. Determine your percent by mass of each of your trials.

$$\% \text{ by mass} = \frac{\text{mass of } CH_3COOH}{\text{mass of vinegar}}$$

Part 4: What did you learn?

a. Is it true that commercial vinegar is approximately 5% by mass? Explain.

b. List two sources of experimental error that may have affected your results.

c. If you "overtitrated" and your solution was too pink, how would this affect your percent by mass of acetic acid? Explain.

d. Show the Lewis structure of acetic acid (CH_3COOH).

e. Which hydrogen atom is the one that is lost when acetic acid reacts with the base (NaOH)?

f. When the "endpoint" of your titration is reached, what should be true about the moles of acid and the moles of base? Explain.

13C: Commercial Antacids

How do antacids work? Are some antacids more effective than others?

Our stomach produces acid to help us digest our food and to protect us against bacterial infection. An average sized adult produces between two and three liters of gastric juice each day. The type of acid produced in our stomach is HCl. Sometimes the body produces too much acid, and it can cause discomfort. Antacid tablets are designed to help neutralize some of the excess acid our body produces. Antacids are bases, providing OH^- to react with extra acid (H^+), giving water as a product. Some foods that are spicy, or fatty or that contain caffeine are more likely to give us acid indigestion.

Materials
• Mortar and pestle
• 100 mL of 0.1 M HCl
• 50 mL of 0.1 M NaOH
• Phenolphthalein indicator in a dropper bottle
• Variety of antacid tablets (e.g., Tums®, Rolaids®, Alka-Seltzer®, or Maalox®)
• Distilled water bottle
• 250 mL Erlenmeyer flask
• Mass balance
• 25 mm test tube
• Lab-Master with heater

In this investigation we will use a method called "back-titration" to mimic the process that occurs in our stomachs. We will allow the antacid tablet to react with the HCl in our flask. After the antacid tablet has reacted with as much of the acid as it can, we will titrate the remaining unreacted acid with NaOH. When the antacid and acid react, water is produced, which makes this a neutralization reaction. Some brands of antacids will absorb more acid per gram of tablet. These antacids are considered more effective.

Part 1: Procedure

1. Select your brand of antacid tablet to test.

2. Use the mortar and pestle to grind one antacid tablet into a fine powder. Weigh between 0.2 and 0.3 g of the tablet. You need to know how much of the tablet you titrate. Try to use the same amount in each trial.

3. Transfer your mass of the tablet to a large test tube for heating in the Lab-Master. Carefully measure 25.0 mL of 0.1 M HCl and add it to the test tube containing the antacid.

4. Add 2 or 3 drops of phenolphthalein to the test tube. The solution should be colorless after swirling.

5. Set the heater to 70°C. Bubbling may occur, but avoid spattering. If spattering does occur, turn down the heat. Heat for about 2 minutes.

6. Allow the mixture to cool to room temperature, and then transfer it to a 250 mL Erlenmeyer flask for titration. Rinse the test tube used to heat the tablet and acid with 10 mL of distilled water. Add this rinse to your Erlenmeyer flask. Try to leave as little residue as possible behind in the test tube.

7. If your solution is pink at this point, add HCl in 1.0 mL increments until your solution is colorless. Swirl to mix.

8. Using a dropper bottle, titrate with the 0.10 M NaOH solution until the first sign of permanent pink color persists for more than 30 s. Record the number of drops required. Convert the number of drops to milliliters using your conversion. Record the volume of NaOH used to titrate. (Note: The number of drops per milliliters has been previously determined. If you wish to redetermine or check the amount, you need to carefully count how many drops it takes to reach the 1.0 mL mark in a 10 mL graduated cylinder and then divide by 10.)

9. Repeat this procedure for two more trials of the same antacid.

Part 2: Thinking about it

1. What was the active ingredient in your antacid tablet? Write its chemical formula.

2. Write out the chemical reaction that shows your active ingredient reacting with acid.

3. Make a list of the active ingredients and the names of the antacids the members of your class tested.

4. What might happen if a person consumes too many antacid tablets each day?

5. What was the biggest experimental challenge you faced while performing this experiment? How might this have affected your results?

6. Briefly explain how the acidity of gastric juice helps to digest your food.

Part 3: How effective was your antacid?

1. Using the molarity formula (M = moles/volume), calculate the moles of HCl added to the antacid tablet.

2. Again using the molarity formula, calculate the moles of NaOH you added during the titration.

3. Subtract the moles of NaOH from the moles of HCl. This will provide you with the moles of HCl that were *neutralized* by your antacid.

4. Divide the moles of neutralized HCl by the grams of the antacid tablet you used in Step 2 of Part 1. This number gives you the number of moles of HCl acid that is neutralized per grams of antacid tablet.

5. Multiply by 1,000 to obtain millimoles (mmole) so that you have a larger number to work with. Your units should be (mmole H^+)/(g antacid). You can now compare this value with your other trials.

Here is an example:

$$\text{mass of antacid} = 0.6 \text{ g}$$

$$\text{moles of HCl} = 0.10 \text{ M} \times 0.025 \text{ L} = 0.0025 \text{ moles}$$

$$\text{moles of NaOH} = 0.10 \text{ M} \times 0.005 \text{ L} = 0.0005 \text{ moles}$$

$$\text{moles of HCl neutralized} = \text{moles of HCl} - \text{moles of NaOH}$$

$$= 0.0025 - 0.0005 = 0.002 \text{ moles } H^+$$

$$\frac{\text{moles of HCL neutralized}}{\text{mass of antacid}} = \frac{0.002 \text{ moles } H^+}{0.6 \text{ g}} = 0.0033 \frac{\text{moles } H^+}{\text{g}}$$

$$0.0033 \frac{\text{moles } H^+}{\text{g}} = 3.3 \frac{\text{mmoles } H^+}{\text{g}}$$

6. Average the results of your trials.

Part 4: Analyzing your results

Table 1. Antacid data

Antacid tablet	Active ingredient	Group name	# of trials	Neutralizing power (mmole H^+/g)

a. Based on your class results, which antacid was the most effective at neutralizing stomach acid?

b. How did the antacid you tested compare with the other brands? Explain.

c. Do you think some chemicals are more effective as neutralizing agents? Why or why not?

d. If some of the antacid spattered out of the test tube while heating, how would it affect your results? Explain.

e. If the measurements of the acid added to your tablet were not done carefully by looking at the meniscus, how would it affect your results? Explain.

f. You added the NaOH little by little, looking for a color change in your solution. You determined your endpoint based on your group's judgement of color. How might this have affected your overall class results? Explain.

Part 5: Going further

a. Following the same method used in Step 4 of Part 3, calculate the neutralizing power of 1.0 g of $NaHCO_3$. Assume that each mole of HCO_3^- can neutralize 1 mole of H^+ according to the equation:

$$HCO_3^-(aq) + H^+(aq) \rightarrow H_2CO_3(aq) \rightarrow H_2O(l) + CO_2(g)$$

b. Is this more effective than the antacids you tested? Explain.

c. Sodium bicarbonate can act as an acid or a base because it is amphoteric. This allows HCO_3^- to act as a buffer and neutralize a solution in either direction by absorbing an H^+ ion or releasing an H^+ ion. How do you think the buffering effect could influence your titration with NaOH? Explain.

d. Heating the solution allowed some of the carbon dioxide gas to escape from the solution. How would dissolved CO_2 affect the solution you were titrating? Briefly explain.

13D: Determining the Amount of Vitamin C

How can we determine the amount of ascorbic acid in vitamin C tablets and in different foods?

Ascorbic acid, or vitamin C, is very important for our bodies. Vitamin C is required by our bodies to produce collagen in our connective tissues. Vitamin C thus helps us to maintain healthy teeth, blood vessels, and bones. Vitamin C has also been found to function as an antioxidant, and it aids in the prevention of cancer.

Antioxidants are molecules that can protect our cells from being damaged. Antioxidants such as vitamin C are able to absorb harmful reactive molecules before they can damage our tissues. In this investigation, a titration will be used to determine the amount of vitamin C that is contained in "vitamin C" tablets and in different foods and juices. The recommended daily amount of vitamin C is 60 mg.

Materials

- 250 mL beaker or Erlenmeyer flask
- Vitamin C solution (2 mg/mL), obtained by grinding one 500 mg tablet and dissolving in 250 mL of distilled water
- Dropper bottle
- 10 mL graduated cylinder
- 10 g of starch
- Distilled water bottle
- 20 mL of 0.010 M KIO_3 solution
- 1.0 g KI
- 5.0 mL 1.0 M HCl
- Orange juice and grapefruit juice
- Citrus fruits and juicer
- Cheesecloth
- Medium funnel

We will determine the amount of vitamin C using a simple titration method. The chemical name for vitamin C is ascorbic acid. This procedure relies on a series of chemical reactions that cause an observable color change to occur. To help you better understand what you are seeing when the color change occurs, it is helpful to review some relevant chemical reactions.

In equation two, Vitamin C reacts with iodine (I_2) and becomes oxidized. This is the most important chemical reaction taking place. However, to produce the iodine (I_2) we must first carry out another reaction. Adding solid potassium iodide (KI) and hydrochloric acid (HCl) and the titrant, potassium iodate (KIO_3), creates iodine and water according to the following reaction:

$$1) \quad IO_3^- + 5I^- + 6H^+ \rightarrow 3I_2 + 3H_2O$$

As soon as the iodine (I_2) is created it reacts with the vitamin C, causing the vitamin C to become oxidized.

$$2) \quad I_2 + C_6H_8O_6 \rightarrow C_6H_6O_6 + 2H^+ + 2I^-$$

vitamin C   oxidized
vitamin C

Investigation 13D: Determining the Amount of Vitamin C

After all of the vitamin C has reacted, the I_2 concentration builds up and then begins to react with I^- in solution to form the triiodide ion (I_3^-). The triiodide ion complexes with the starch to give a deep bluish-black color that we can see:

$$I_2 + I^- \rightarrow I_3^- \text{ and } I_3^- + \text{starch} \rightarrow \text{iodide–starch complex}$$
$$\text{deep blue color}$$

When this color appears, we know all of the vitamin C has reacted. *It is the formation of the triiodide ion that signals the endpoint of the titration.*

Once we know how much titrant (KIO_3) is required to reach the endpoint, we can use the volume of KIO_3 to determine the moles of KIO_3. Using stoichiometry we can use the moles of KIO_3 to find the moles of iodine (I_2) and therefore the moles of vitamin C present in our experiment.

Part 1: Calibrate your dropper bottle or pipette

1. We need to accurately determine the number of drops in 1.0 mL. To accomplish this, use either a dropper bottle or a plastic beral pipet. [In Part 2, be sure you add the titrant (KIO_3) using the same dropper and method].

2. To calibrate your dropper, slowly add drops of water to a small 10.0 mL graduated cylinder. Stop adding drops when the meniscus is on the 1.0 mL mark. Record the number of drops you added.

3. Next count how many drops it takes to get to the 2.0 mL mark. Record your measurement. If the number of drops is in close agreement, take the average. If your number of drops does not agree, repeat Steps 2 and 3.

Part 2: Verifying the amount of vitamin C in a commercial tablet

1. Measure 25.0 mL of the vitamin C stock solution, and add it to a 250 mL Erlenmeyer flask. Your instructor will have prepared this ahead of time. Record the concentration of the stock solution in your lab notebook.

2. Prepare a 1% starch solution.

3. Measure 1.0 g of KI solid and add it to the Erlenmeyer flask. Swirl to dissolve.

4. Add 5.0 mL of 1.0 M HCl to the Erlenmeyer flask.

5. Add 2–3 mL of the *fresh* 1.0% starch solution indicator to the Erlenmeyer flask. Swirl to mix.

6. Obtain a dropper bottle of 0.010 M KIO_3 titrant solution. This dropper bottle should be the same type as the one you used in Part 1. If your instructor has the titrant in a stock bottle, measure about 25.0 mL of the 0.010 M KIO_3 titrant solution in a clean, dry beaker and add it to a dropper bottle yourself.

7. Now you are ready to titrate. Add 0.010 M KIO_3 solution drop by drop to the Erlenmeyer flask. Swirl after every few drops. Initially you will see the deep blue color appear in the area that the drop is added. Once you begin to see a deep blue color that persists throughout the solution, add the titrant more slowly and swirl after every drop. Continue adding titrant until you obtain a

114

A Natural Approach to Chemistry

permanent blue color that lasts about 60 s. Record the total number of drops you added. The solution may lighten after the 60 s, but it should remain fairly deep blue. Determining the "right" color takes practice and is somewhat objective. Do your best, and then repeat the experiment. After two or three trials, you will feel more confident at determining your endpoint.

Part 3: How much vitamin C is there in different fruits and juices?

Here we will determine the vitamin C content of a food of your choice. You may use citrus fruits, fresh squeezed or prepared, apple juice, or any drink containing ascorbic acid. Real lemon juice also makes a nice sample to test, and the amount of vitamin C is on the label.

1. To begin you may use fresh or prepared juice. You will need about 25 mL of juice to have enough vitamin C for a good measurement. If you use freshly squeezed juice, it is helpful to strain out the pulp with cheesecloth. An easy way to strain out the pulp is to use a funnel lined with two or three layers of cheesecloth. Pour the sample of juice through the cheesecloth and collect the juice. Record the exact volume of juice you will titrate.

2. Add your juice to a 250 mL Erlenmeyer flask.

3. Titrate your sample using the same steps you used to titrate the vitamin C tablet. Be sure to add 1.0 g of solid KI, 5.0 mL of 1.0 M HCl and 2–3 mL of starch solution.
   Note: You may not see the deep blue color because of the color of your fruit juice. For instance, it may appear brownish instead of blue. This is fine; just be sure you look for the same color change in each trial. That is the key.

4. Repeat your experiment two or three times to obtain an accurate sense of the reproducibility of your results. Record your results and find the average amount of vitamin C in your sample.

Part 4: Thinking about it

1. Make a data table that records the number of drops of 0.010 M KIO_3 needed to titrate 25 mL of the vitamin C stock solution.

2. Convert your drops to milliliters using the conversion you determined in Part 1. Record this in your data table. Here is an example:

   25 drops = 1 mL

   Used 154 drops of KIO_3 to titrate

   $$154 \text{ drops} \times \frac{1 \text{ mL}}{25 \text{ drops}} = 6.16 \text{ mL}$$

3. Does it matter how much distilled water was added to your sample? Explain.

4. Which contained more vitamin C: the tablet or the food? How do you know?

5. Look carefully at the first equation on page 113. Copy this equation into your lab notebook. Which substance was the reducing agent? Explain. Which substance was the oxidizing agent? Explain.

Part 5: What did you obtain for results?

1. Use the volume of your KIO_3 titrant added in liters and the known molarity (0.010 M) to calculate the moles of KIO_3 required to titrate the vitamin C sample, as shown in this example:

$$M = \frac{mole}{L}$$

$$0.010\ M = \frac{moles\ KIO_3}{0.00616\ L}$$

2. Using the second equation on page 113 and stoichiometry, convert the moles of KIO_3 to moles of I_2 produced. See the example calculation shown in Step 3.

$$moles\ of\ KIO_3 = 6.16 \times 10^5$$

3. Calculate your moles of vitamin C, from the amount of I_2 produced in Step 2. Use the first equation on page 113, stoichiometry, and the following example to help you with this calculation:

$$6.16 \times 10^{-5}\ moles\ KIO_3 \times \frac{3\ moles\ I_2}{1\ mole\ KIO_3} = 1.85 \times 10^{-4}\ moles\ I_2$$

$$6.85 \times 10^{-4}\ moles\ I_2 \times \frac{1\ mole\ C_6H_8O_6\ (vit.\ C)}{1\ mole\ I_2} = 1.85 \times 10^{-4}\ moles\ of\ C_6H_8O_6$$

4. Calculate the grams of vitamin C from the moles of vitamin C you determined.

5. Convert your grams to milligrams by dividing by 1,000. This number tells you how many milligrams of vitamin C were in your 25.0 mL sample of the vitamin C stock solution, or your food.

6. Which food contained the highest amount of vitamin C? Explain.

7. The stock solution contained a 500 mg tablet of vitamin C and 250 mL of distilled water. Combine your results with those of your classmates and see how close your results came to this value. For example, if each group titrated 25.0 mL of stock solution, then the total milligrams in 10 trials would give you a total volume of 250 mL of solution, and this should give you a value close to 500 mg of vitamin C. To estimate, you could also take your trial average and multiply the number of milligrams by 10 to see if you are close to 500 mg.

8. Based on your result, does a 500 mg tablet really contain 500 mg of vitamin C?

9. If the recommended daily allowance of vitamin C is 60 mg, how much of your food would you need to consume to get your daily allowance? Show your calculation.

A NATURAL APPROACH TO
CHEMISTRY

14A: Determination of Butane's Molar Mass

What is the molar mass of butane? How can the ideal gas law be applied to real life?

Butane is a common fuel used in disposable lighters. In this investigation, we will use a disposable lighter and collect butane gas over water. This will provide us with a gaseous sample of butane to experiment with. Using this sample we will measure the volume, temperature, and pressure of the butane gas. From your data, you will be able to determine the molar mass of butane. The molar mass will be used to find the chemical formula for butane.

Materials

- Two 250 mL graduated cylinders
- Butane lighter
- Pneumatic trough (plastic tub)
- Lab-Master with temperature probe
- CRC Handbook (or online guide)
- Mass balance
- Hair dryer

It is helpful to have a pneumatic trough that is tall enough on the sides so that the height of the water can be adjusted with the height of the water column in the graduated cylinder. If the plastic trough is too shallow, you will need to adjust the pressure to include the height of the water column.

Part 1: Procedure

It is helpful to have two groups set up and work together using the same pneumatic trough and lighter.

1. Obtain a new disposable lighter and remove the flint, wheel, and spring as demonstrated by your instructor. Once they are removed, weigh the lighter to the nearest 0.1 g and record your measurement.

2. Fill a 250 mL graduated cylinder all the way to the top so that there is no room for air when you invert it in the plastic trough. If there are air bubbles, just remove the graduated cylinder, refill it with water, and try again. Use a ring stand to hold your graduated cylinder so that the mouth is submerged but it is off the bottom of the trough.

3. Repeat Step 2 with a second 250 mL graduated cylinder. You may set this up in the same pneumatic trough; just separate them a little.

4. Submerge the lighter underwater and hold it below, and just up inside, the mouth of the 250 mL graduated cylinder. Press the button on the lighter so that the gas escapes. Watch carefully to see that all of the bubbles of the gas go up inside the graduated cylinder. Hold the button down until you have about 200 mL of gas.

Investigation 14A: Determination of Butane's Molar Mass

5. Record the exact volume of gas in the graduated cylinder.

6. If there is a height difference between the water level in the trough and the water level in the graduated cylinder, try to adjust the position of the cylinder in the water so that water levels inside and outside the cylinder are the same. If this cannot be done, use a ruler and measure the height difference from the surface of the water in the trough to the water level inside the graduated cylinder. Use the centimeter side of the ruler. Save this information; we will use it in Part 3d.

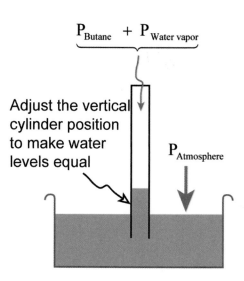

$P_{Butane} + P_{Water vapor}$

Adjust the vertical cylinder position to make water levels equal

$P_{Atmosphere}$

7. Now the next group uses the same lighter to collect another 200 mL of gas in the second prepared 250 mL graduated cylinder.

8. Repeat Steps 4 and 5 for this gas collection.

9. When done, shake excess water from the lighter and dry with a paper towel. Let it sit to dry while you finish with your measurements. It needs to be dry before you reweigh it.

10. Use your Lab-Master and temperature probe to measure the temperature of the water in the trough. (We will assume that the gas will be at the same temperature as the water.) Look up the vapor pressure for water at this temperature in the CRC Handbook or as instructed by your teacher.

11. To calculate the partial pressure of butane gas, you will need to know the current barometric pressure (air pressure). Your instructor will either provide it for you or show you how to obtain this information.

12. Empty your trough and clean up your work area.

13. Reweigh your disposable lighter, if dry. You may use a hair dryer on a *low* setting to speed up the drying process. The lighter must be completely dry, as the mass difference is very small from start to finish.

Table 1. Data table

	Trial 1	Trial 2
Volume of butane (mL)		
Temperature of water (°C)		
Barometric pressure (atm)		
Water vapor pressure (atm)		
Mass of lighter (before)		
Mass of lighter (after)		

118

A NATURAL APPROACH TO CHEMISTRY

Part 2: Calculating the molar mass

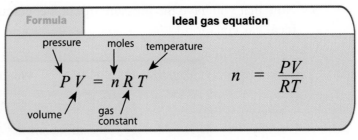

1. To use the ideal gas equation to calculate the moles (n) of butane, you must first obtain each of the variables in the formula.
(Use R = 0.08206 atm·L/mole·K for the gas constant)

2. Your volume measurement can be obtained directly from your data and so can your temperature, but the pressure (P) for butane must be calculated using Dalton's law of partial pressures:

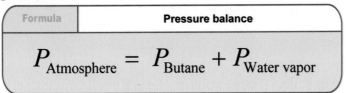

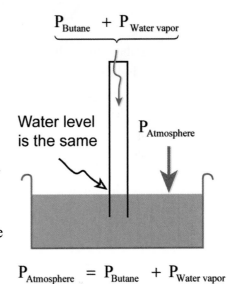

By making the water level inside the tube equal to the water level outside the tub, the pressure inside the tube is equal to the pressure outside.
The pressure inside the tube is $P_{Butane} + P_{Water\ vapor}$ and the pressure outside is the atmospheric pressure ($P_{Atmosphere}$).
The pressure for butane is

$$P_{Butane} = P_{Atmosphere} - P_{Water\ vapor}$$

All units need to be the same (agree) to use the formula. In the end your P_{butane} value needs to be in atmospheres (atm) to have your units cancel using the ideal gas constant as given.

If the water inside the tube is not at the same level as the water outside, there is an additional pressure component that must be taken into account. It is the pressure equivalent of the water column. This pressure is:

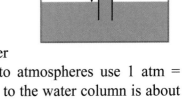

$$P_{Water\ column} = \rho g h$$

The density (ρ) is that of water (1,000 kg/m^3),
the gravitational acceleration (g) is (9.8 m/sec^2), and
the height (h) is given in meters so that the pressure of the water column is in newtons per square meter, or pascals. To convert to atmospheres use 1 atm = 101,300 Pa. For example, if the height h is 10 cm the pressure due to the water column is about 0.01 atm.
The pressure for the butane is: $P_{butane} = P_{Atmosphere} - P_{Water\ vapor} - P_{Water\ column}$
If the water level inside the tube is lower than the water level outside the butane pressure is
$$P_{Butane} = P_{Atmosphere} - P_{Water\ vapor} + P_{Water\ column}$$

3. Now that you have the pressure of butane, calculate the number of moles of butane (n) using the ideal gas equation.

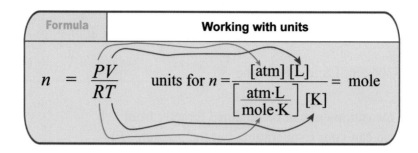

4. Calculate the molar mass of the butane using the mass of the gas (difference in mass of lighter) and dividing it by the number of moles (n) you obtained in Step 3.

Part 3: Thinking it through

a. Can you speculate why is it necessary to collect a large volume of gas from the lighter? (Hint: Think about the method used to determine the amount of butane used.)

b. Is butane a liquid or a gas when it is inside the lighter? Discuss your ideas with your classmates.

c. Why was it important to account for the water vapor pressure? Explain using Dalton's law of partial pressure.

d. If the water level inside the graduated cylinder is above the water level in your tub, then you needed to measure how high it was. Explain why you might or might not need to account for this height difference in your calculations. To do this, you must calculate the pressure resulting from the difference in height and compare it to the other terms in the pressure balance formula.

e. We made some assumptions when collecting our data. List at least two.

f. What do you think the largest source of error was in this experiment? Support your answer with evidence.

g. The percent composition of butane in the lighter is 82.63% carbon and 17.37% hydrogen. From this information, calculate the empirical formula for butane.

h. Using your molar mass, try to obtain the molecular formula for butane.
(Hint: You need to get close to a whole number multiple when you divide the molar mass by the empirical mass you obtained. If it is not a whole number, then you will need to round.)

A NATURAL APPROACH TO
CHEMISTRY

14B: Density of Air

How heavy is air?

Air might seem like "nothing," but air is matter just like water is matter. Air is made up of atoms and molecules, and it has considerable mass. In this investigation, you will measure the density of air and compare it to the density of a solid and a liquid.

Materials

- Mass balance
- 1 L plastic soda bottle
- Prepared bottle cap with inserted tire valve
- Tire pressure gauge
- Bicycle pump
- Large graduated cylinder

Part 1: The gas phase

Safety Note: Be careful with the bottle, and *do not* exceed 70 pounds per square inch (psi) of pressure.

1. Get the prepared cap with the tire valve and a 1 L carbonated soda bottle. (Do not use a plastic water bottle.)

2. Fill the bottle to the very top with water. Empty the water into a graduated cylinder to measure the volume of the bottle. Record the volume in Table 1.

3. Put the valve cap on the empty bottle (full of air) and measure the mass. This is the mass of the bottle and the air it contains at zero gauge pressure. Record the mass in Table 1.

4. Use the bicycle pump to raise the pressure in the bottle to 10 psi. Check the pressure with your gauge.

5. Use the balance to measure and record the mass of the bottle (and air) at 10 psi pressure.

6. Repeat the pumping and mass measurement for pressures between 10 psi and 70 psi. *Do not* exceed 70 psi!

Table 1. Pressure and mass data

Gauge pressure (psi)	Mass (g)	Volume (ml)

Part 2: Thinking about what you observed

a. What happens to the mass as you increase the pressure in the bottle?

b. Explain what causes the relationship you observed in Part 2a.

Part 3: Graphing the data

Now we convert gauge pressure to actual, or absolute, pressure by adding 14.7 psi (1 atm) to gauge pressure.

Table 2. Calculating the mass of air

Gauge pressure (psi)	Absolute pressure (psi)	Mass of bottle and air (g)		Mass of bottle at zero gauge pressure (g)		Mass of air added to bottle (g)
			−		=	
			−		=	
			−		=	
			−		=	
			−		=	
			−		=	
			−		=	

a. Use Table 2 to calculate the mass of air added to the bottle at different pressures.

b. Make a graph showing the mass of air plotted against the pressure.

c. When the pressure is zero on the gauge, is there any air in the bottle? Use the graph (or your data) to estimate the mass of air in the bottle at atmospheric pressure (zero on the gauge).

Part 4: Liquid and solid phases

1. Use your balance to measure out a quantity of water of equal mass to the air at zero gauge pressure.

2. Use your balance to measure out a quantity of solid material (coins, salt, or sugar work well) of equal mass to the air at zero gauge pressure. (Use these data to answer the questions in Part 5.)

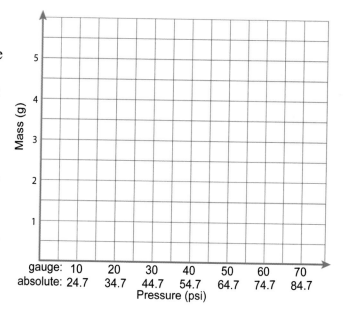

Part 5: Thinking about what you observed

a. Compare the total amount of matter in the gas, liquid, and solid samples. Does one have more matter? Does one have less matter? Or, do all have about the same amount of matter?

b. How does the number of atoms compare in each of the three samples (solid, liquid, and gas)? How can the number of atoms be different if the total mass is the same?

c. Calculate the density of each of the three samples (solid, liquid, and gas). Perform your calculation in units of grams per milliliter (or g/cm^3). For the air, use the highest pressure you measured.

d. The density of one of the samples changed a great deal during the experiment. Calculate the highest and lowest density you observed for the sample that changed the most.

e. Propose an explanation for why the density changed so much in the gas sample.

122

15A: The Lemon Battery

What kind of chemistry creates electricity in a battery?

Everything on Earth stores and uses energy to stay alive. The ultimate source of this energy is the Sun. By what process does life collect and store its energy? In this experiment, you will see how the process of energy storage (and use) in living things is described by electrochemistry! Both we and the lemon are living batteries!

Materials

- Lemon
- Small knife
- Light emitting diode (LED)
- 5 cm piece of copper wire
- 5 cm piece of magnesium ribbon
- Two clip leads (red and black)
- Lab-Master with voltage probe

Part 1: Making a lemon light up

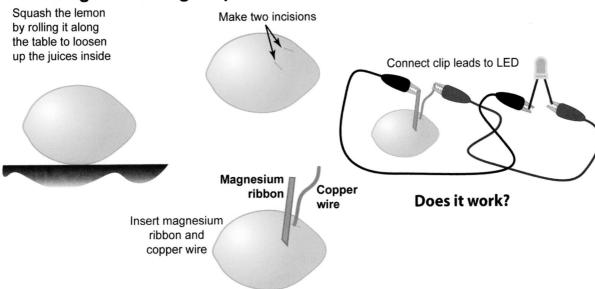

Squash the lemon by rolling it along the table to loosen up the juices inside

Make two incisions

Connect clip leads to LED

Magnesium ribbon   Copper wire

Insert magnesium ribbon and copper wire

Does it work?

1. Roll the lemon on a table so that the juice can flow easily.

2. Using a small knife, make two small incisions on the lemon about 2 cm apart.

3. Insert the piece of magnesium into one incision and the piece of copper into the other incision.

4. Use the clip leads to connect the leads of the LED to the copper wire and the magnesium ribbon.

5. The LED should light up. If the LED does not light, switch the way that the LED leads are connected to the copper and the magnesium.

Part 2: What just happened?

a. Why did the LED light up?

b. Where did the electricity come from?

Investigation 15A: The Lemon Battery

Part 3: Try something new

1. What happens if you replace the magnesium ribbon with a copper wire? Does the LED light?
2. What happens to the intensity of the light if you use two copper wires and two magnesium ribbons? Does the light intensity increase, stay the same, or decrease?

Part 4: Let's measure the electricity that comes out of the lemon

1. Connect the red alligator clip of the voltage probe to the copper wire and the black alligator clip to the magnesium ribbon.

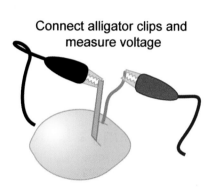

Connect alligator clips and measure voltage

2. Connect the voltage probe to the probe system and measure the voltage.
3. Insert a second copper wire and a second magnesium ribbon into the incisions and measure the voltage.
4. Now reverse the red and black alligator clips and measure the voltage again.

Part 5: Did you observe this?

a. What happened to the voltage reading when you inserted the second piece of copper wire and magnesium ribbon?

b. If the voltage reading did not change, how do you explain the increase in the intensity of the light when you doubled up the copper and the magnesium?

c. If the two pieces of metal that are inserted into the lemon are the same the LED does not light. Why? Does this mean that the choice of metal somehow affects the experiment?

d. Look closely at the place where the Mg and Cu ribbons are inserted into the lemon. Do you see any bubbles? If so, there must be gas formed inside the lemon. What do you think that gas is?

e. There is an engineering connection here. What if this was indeed a battery, and besides the electricity it also generated gas. What can you say about the efficiency of such a battery? Do you think that having a battery that also generates gas is a good thing, a bad thing, or doesn't matter? Explain your answer.

Part 6: Another variation

1. Replace the copper wire with a zinc-coated (galvanized) nail.
2. Connect the red alligator clip of the voltage probe to the zinc nail and the black alligator clip to the magnesium.
3. What is the voltage reading now?
4. Is it higher or lower than the case with the magnesium and copper?
5. If you connect the LED as you did in Part 1, does it light up?
6. Do you think that the type of metal has something to do with the voltage that is generated?

124

15B: An Electrochemical Cell

How do batteries store energy?

Batteries store chemical energy and convert it to electrical energy by connecting the positive and the negative terminals. When the terminals are connected, electricity flows. The flow of electricity is a result of a chemical reaction that takes place inside the battery. The chemical reaction depends on the materials that the battery is made of.

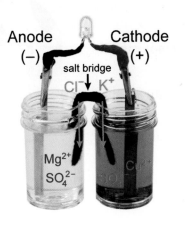

Materials

- 1 M solution of MgSO$_4$ (epsom salt)
- 1 M solution of CuSO$_4$
- One light emitting diode (LED)
- One 5 cm piece of bare copper wire
- One 5 cm piece of magnesium ribbon
- One 10 cm piece of copper wire with stripped ends
- Two (red and black) wires with alligator clips
- Two small vials
- One A and B holding tray
- A piece of felt cloth or filter paper 5 × 50 mm
- 1 M sodium chloride (NaCl) solution
- Lab-Master with voltage probe

Part 1: The Voltaic cell

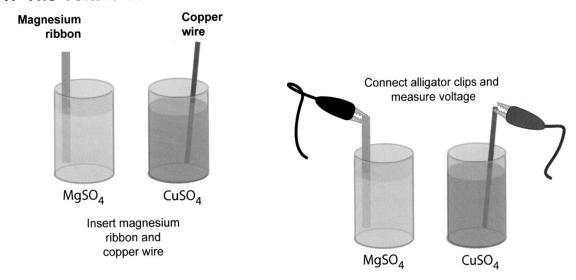

1. Fill one vial 3/4 full with MgSO$_4$ solution and the other 3/4 full with CuSO$_4$ solution. Place them in the holding tray.
2. Place the magnesium ribbon in the MgSO$_4$ solution and the copper wire in the CuSO$_4$ solution.
3. Connect the red alligator clip of the voltage probe to the copper wire and the black alligator clip to the magnesium ribbon.
4. Turn on the Lab-Master and measure the voltage.

Part 2: What did you observe?

1. What happened when you tried to measure the voltage with the voltmeter?
2. Does it make sense that the voltage is zero?

Part 3: Try something new

1. Now take a piece of copper wire, bend it into a U shape, and place it as a bridge connecting the test tubes as indicated in the drawing.

2. What is the voltage reading now?

3. What happens to the voltage reading if you remove the U-shaped piece of copper wire?

4. Leave the wire in place for about 3 minutes. Remove the wire and look at the two ends.

5. What do you observe? What happened to the color of the Mg and Cu wires that were in the solution?

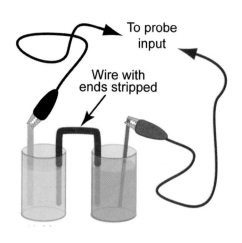

To probe input

Wire with ends stripped

Part 4: Learn about the salt bridge

1. Soak the filter paper or felt cloth in the NaCl solution and place it as a bridge connecting the two vials. This is the "salt bridge."

2. Measure the voltage between the copper wire and the magnesium ribbon with the voltmeter.

3. What voltage do you read?

4. What happens when you switch the connection of the red and the black alligator clips?

5. What happens to the voltage reading if you remove the salt bridge?

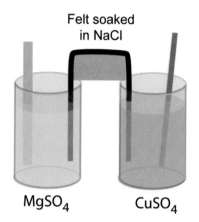

Adding the salt bridge

Felt soaked in NaCl

$MgSO_4$ $CuSO_4$

Part 5: Is this a real battery?

1. Use the clip leads to connect the LED to the magnesium ribbon and the copper wire.

2. If the LED does not light up, switch the way that the LED is connected to the magnesium and the copper. Why does switching the connections to the LED make a difference? (Hint: A diode is an electrical device that only allows current to flow in one direction, like a one-way street.)

3. Try connecting two pieces of copper and/or two pieces of magnesium. Does the intensity of the light coming from the LED change? Can you think of a possible explanation for the change or the lack of change?

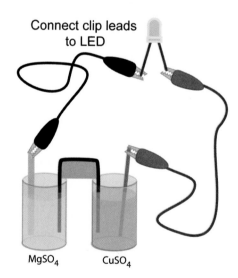

Connect clip leads to LED

$MgSO_4$ $CuSO_4$

A NATURAL APPROACH TO
CHEMISTRY

15C: Oxidation–Reduction Reactions of Metals and Metal Ions

Which metals tend to lose electrons? Which metallic ions tend to gain electrons?

In this investigation you will set up an *activity series* for some metals. An activity series arranges metals according to their ability to be oxidized. As you will see, some metals lose electrons more easily than others.

Materials
• One strip (10 cm) of each: Cu, Zn, Fe, and Sn
• One dropper bottle of 0.10 M solution of each: $Cu(NO_3)_2$, $Zn(NO_3)_2$, $AgNO_3$, and $Fe(NO_3)_2$
• Steel wool
• Distilled water bottle
• Waste disposal container for heavy metals

Part 1: Procedure

1. Use steel wool to clean off one side of each of your metal strips.

2. Make some observations about your metal strips. Note each one's color and malleability. It is important that you can distinguish which metal is which. It is a good idea to label them with tape and a marker, because some of them may look similar to you.

3. Arrange your metal strips in the same order as shown on Table 1. Using the dropper bottles, place one drop of each of the aqueous metal ion solutions. Test only one solution at a time so that you do not get confused about which solution is causing the reaction. Once the drop is placed on the metal strip, it may take a minute or so for the reaction to occur. However, no more than a couple of minutes should be needed. In most cases the reaction will occur right away.

4. Fill in the data in Table 1 as you perform tests. Write RXN (if a reaction occurred) or NR (if no reaction occurred).

Table 1. Reaction of metals with metal ions

Metals	Ions			
	Ag^+	Zn^{2+}	Cu^{2+}	Fe^{2+}
Zn				
Cu				
Fe				
Sn				

5. Rinse off each of the metal strips with tap water and dry them with a paper towel. Return them to the appropriately labeled beaker.

Part 2: Writing the chemical equations

We will write out reactions *only* for the tests that caused a reaction. It is not necessary to write the combinations that did not result in an obvious reaction.

1. Refer to your table and write down the reactant solutions for one reaction. For example:

$$Zn(s) + Cu(NO_3)_2(aq) \rightarrow$$

2. Separate the reactant ions in the aqueous solution. For example:

$$Zn(s) + Cu^{2+}(aq) + 2NO_3^-(aq) \rightarrow$$

3. This is an example of a "single replacement" reaction where one metal "replaces" the other metal. A single replacement reaction is an oxidation–reduction reaction. In this case the solid metal gets oxidized and the metal ion gets reduced.

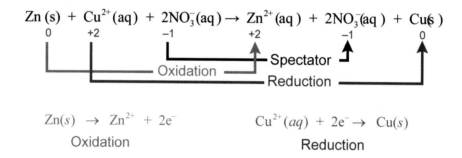

Write out the reactions that occurred for each metal strip in the manner shown above. List the half reactions for each separately. Recall that nitrate (NO_3^-) is a spectator ion and is NOT involved in the reaction.

(*Note*: There will be times when you need to balance your chemical reactions so that the number of electrons being lost are equal to the number of electrons being gained. This will occur when you are using a metal such as Zn that forms a +2 ion and a metal ion such as Ag that forms a +1 ion.)

Part 3: Activity series

1. Make a list that organizes the metals strips you tested. Arrange them from *most* easily oxidized to least easily oxidized.

2. Make another list of your metal ion half-reactions. Organize these from *most* easily reduced to least easily reduced.

Part 4: What did you learn?

1. Describe what you learned about the metal strips you tested.
2. How would an activity series be helpful to a chemist?
3. Give a practical example of an metal oxidizing in your everyday life.
4. Why is the nitrate anion not shown in your half-reactions? Explain.

CHEMISTRY

15D: Electroplating

What is the chemistry of electroplating?

Brass is a soft gold-colored metal that is easy to machine, and is often used for faucets and doorknobs. Unfortunately, brass tarnishes easily. The solution is to electroplate chromium on brass to give it a more durable surface. Chromium is a silver-colored metal that does not tarnish, staying bright and shiny. How does this process work? In this investigation, you will electroplate copper metal onto a steel electrode. The electrochemical process is identical to the one used to chrome-plate your bathroom faucet!

Materials

- 1 M CuSO$_4$ solution
- One 9 V battery
- Scouring pad or extra fine sandpaper
- Two stainless steel electrodes
- 25 mm test tube
- Two hole stopper
- Ring stand with test tube clamp or test tube rack
- Red and black wire leads with alligator clips

Part 1: The experiment

1. Connect the apparatus as shown in the diagram. The test tube should be held in a test tube clamp in a ring stand (not shown).

2. Make sure the electrodes are clean. Use fine sandpaper or a scouring pad if needed.

3. Fill a test tube half full with copper sulfate (CuSO$_4$) solution and loosely insert the stopper with the electrodes. *Do not tighten the stopper* as gas must be allowed to escape.

4. Connect the positive terminal of a 9 V battery to one electrode.

5. Connect the other clip lead to the second electrode and touch it to the 9 V battery. Make careful observations of what you see at each electrode in Table 1 below.

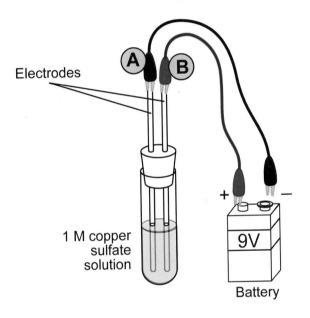

6. After 2–3 s, disconnect the wires from the electrodes. Remove the stopper with the electrodes and examine them carefully.

7. You can clean the electrodes off with the sandpaper and try the experiment several times. Play with the device and record any additional interesting observations in Table 1.

Table 1. Observations for the electroplating experiment

	Positive electrode	Negative electrode
Bubbling (yes/no)		
Color change (describe)		
Effect of removing wire		

Part 2: Explaining what happened

a. Which electrode showed bubbling, the one connected to the positive terminal or the one connected to the negative terminal of the battery?

b. Which electrode showed copper plating?

c. Did you observe any temperature change?

d. What happened to the reaction when either wire was disconnected?

Part 3: Understanding the chemistry

There are three reactions that might occur in the test tube. Use the diagram below to match the words and reactions to the correct electrode. Sketch in the battery connections as well.

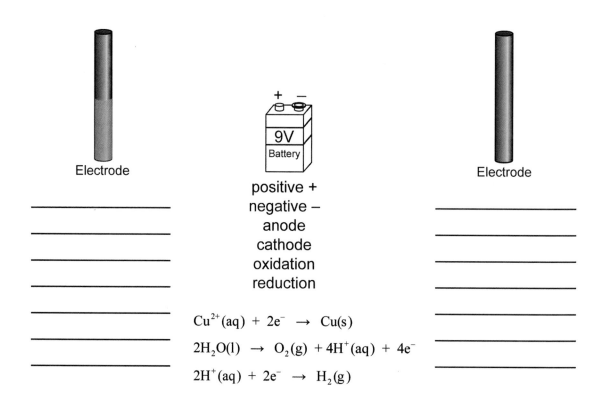

Electrode

Electrode

positive +
negative –
anode
cathode
oxidation
reduction

$Cu^{2+}(aq) + 2e^- \rightarrow Cu(s)$

$2H_2O(l) \rightarrow O_2(g) + 4H^+(aq) + 4e^-$

$2H^+(aq) + 2e^- \rightarrow H_2(g)$

a. What is the gas given off by the reaction? Explain your reasoning.

b. Can you think of a way to test your answer to Question a?

c. What happens to the sulfate ion left in the solution?

d. As the electroplating reaction progresses, do you think the pH of the solution will change? If so, will it become more acidic, more basic, or more neutral? Explain why you think so.

e. If a copper electrode is used as the anode, it is observed that the copper is eaten away. It is also observed that the solution stays deep blue instead of gradually getting lighter. Write down a reaction that would explain these observations.

A NATURAL APPROACH TO
CHEMISTRY

16A: Surface Tension and Surfactants

What is surface tension? How can we observe it? How can we change it?

Surface tension is a property of liquids that is both fascinating and useful. Water has a high surface tension, and you have probably seen this when you fill a glass too high. You may have noticed that sometimes it doesn't spill! Surface tension is what keeps the water from spilling. Objects that are denser than water can appear to float, when in reality it is the force of surface tension that is keeping them from sinking. Surfactants, such as soaps and detergents, can be used to lower the surface tension of water.

Materials
• Water
• One clean 25 mm test tube
• Two clean 50 mL beakers
• One pipette
• Tweezers
• Soap solution in a dropper
• Paper clip, staple, and a dime
• Vegetable oil

Part 1: Exploring surface tension

Fill a test tube almost to the top with water. Then, using a pipette carefully add water to the test tube until it is "full," or filled exactly to the top of the test tube. Finally, continue adding drops of water to the test tube. Count how many drops you can add after the test tube was "full," before the liquid spills out of the test tube.

1. There are about 25 drops of water in 1 mL. How many milliliters of water did you add to the test tube after it was full before it spilled?

2. Suppose you had done this experiment with a wider container, like a bowl. Do you think you would have been able to add more, less, or the same amount of water to a full bowl than you did for the test tube before spilling the water?

Part 2: Surface tension supports weight

1. Fill a clean 50 mL beaker with water.

2. Using tweezers, *carefully* hold a paper clip close to the surface of the water. Poke the surface of the water with the edge of the paper clip. What happens?

3. Now try to *very carefully* place the paper clip on the surface of the water, making it "float." Remember, it isn't really floating! What do you observe about the surface of the water near the paper clip? (An easy way to float the paper clip is to place it on a piece of tissue paper and then place the paper along with the paper clip on the water. The paper gets wet and sinks, leaving the paper clip on the surface.)

4. Try and experiment to see how heavy of an object can be supported by the surface tension of the water. What else can it support?

Part 3: Surfactants and surface tension

1. Fill a new clean beaker with water.

2. Using tweezers, carefully place a paper clip on the surface of the water so it is supported by surface tension.

3. Now, carefully add a drop of soap solution to the water. What happens? Add more drops if you don't see a change, and record this number of drops.

4. The soap acts as a *surfactant*, lowering the surface tension of water. Where can you find surfactants in your house? What do they do? How does surface tension determine what those surfactants do?

Part 4: Surface tension of other liquids

1. Fill a clean dry beaker with vegetable oil.

2. Repeat the paper clip experiment. Does it "float"?

3. Try to place heavier objects on the surface of the oil. How heavy of an object can the oil surface support?

4. How does the surface tension of oil compare to that of water?

Part 5: Thinking about what we have learned

1. In Part 4, you found that oil has a lower surface tension than water. Why do you think this is? What is different about the way that oil and water molecules bond?

2. How does the amount of polarity in a molecule relate to its surface tension?

3. A stream of water will spontaneously separate into droplets of water. Provide an explanation for this phenomenon using surface tension.

4. Provide some examples in nature where surface tension helps a plant or an animal.

5. How do you think trees gets the water they need to their branches and leaves?

6. How would you design an experiment to measure surface tension?

A NATURAL APPROACH TO
CHEMISTRY

16B: Measuring Viscosity

What is viscosity? How can we measure and experience it?

Viscosity is the resistance of a liquid to flow. You have probably experienced liquids with different viscosities in your life. In this investigation, we will explore how liquids with different viscosities behave. We will also measure viscosity using a simple system and explore the origins of why some liquids are more viscous than others.

Materials

- Water
- Disposable gloves
- Clean 250 mL beakers
- Vegetable oil (olive, corn, peanut, safflower, or other)
- Castor oil
- Powdered sugar
- Beral pipette
- A stopwatch or the Lab-Master

Part 1: Exploring viscosity

a. Fill three beakers with 50–100 mL of the following liquids: water, vegetable oil, and castor oil.

b. Using a gloved finger, swirl each liquid around. Note how easily your finger moves through each liquid. This is a quick way to judge relative viscosities of liquids.

c. Arrange the liquids according to their viscosity from highest to lowest.

Part 2: Measuring viscosity

1. Draw two lines on the large dropper as shown in the picture on the right. The exact level is not important.

2. Fill the large dropper with water to the top line.

3. Have a partner get ready to time how long it takes for the liquid to drain from the top line to the bottom line.

4. Carefully twist the red bulb off the dropper, and have your partner time how long it takes for the liquid to drain to the bottom line.

5. Repeat Steps 1–4 five times. Record the average time each liquid takes to drain.

6. Repeat Steps 1–5 for vegetable oil and castor oil.

7. Make a bar graph by plotting the time it takes for each liquid to drain from the dropper. (See the sample graph on the next page.)

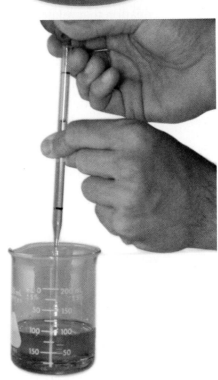

Part 3: Thinking about what we have learned

a. Which liquid is the most viscous? Which liquid is the least viscous?

b. How does the size of the molecule relate to the viscosity of the liquid?

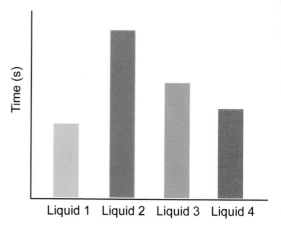

Part 4: The effect of solutes on viscosity

1. Make 100 mL of a saturated solution of powdered sugar in water. To do this, place 100 mL of water in a beaker and keep adding sugar and stirring until no more will dissolve.
2. Pour 20 mL of this solution into four empty beakers. Label the beakers 1, 2, 3, and 4.
3. Dilute beaker 1 with 60 mL of water to create a 1/4 saturated sugar solution.
4. Dilute beaker 2 with 20 mL of water to create a 1/2 saturated sugar solution.
5. Dilute beaker 3 with 7 mL of water to create a 3/4 saturated sugar solution.
6. Repeat the experiment in Part 2, measuring the time it takes to drain from the top line to the bottom line for each liquid five times. Graph the average time needed for each liquid to drain on the same graph as the liquids in Part 2.

Part 5: Think about what we have learned

1. How did the viscosity of the sugar solution change with the concentration of sugar? Develop an equation that relates the concentration of sugar in water to its viscosity. Don't forget to include pure water (0% sugar).
2. Why do you think the viscosity of a solution increases with more solute?
3. How do you think the viscosity of pancake syrup compares to that of your saturated sugar solution? How would you make a syrup that has more sugar than your saturated sugar solution (a supersaturated solution)?
4. Explain how the shape and bonding in a molecule relates to its viscosity.
5. Why did we run each experiment five times? How does that help us make our experiment more accurate?
6. Suggest three ways to make this experiment more precise and reduce the error.
7. We use liquids with different viscosities in our everyday lives. Give an example of a place where you would want to use a liquid with a very low viscosity (runny). Give an example of a place where you would want to use a liquid with a very high viscosity (sticky).
8. Give examples in nature where a plant or animal uses a low-viscosity liquid to its advantage.
9. Give examples in nature where a plant or animal uses a high-viscosity liquid to its advantage.

A NATURAL APPROACH TO
CHEMISTRY

17A: Oil Spills

How does oil behave upon contact with water? What are the environmental concerns when oil is spilled into the ocean?

You may have observed that oil and water do not mix well. Sometimes we see a film of oil or gasoline on lakes and ponds left behind from motorboats. The nonpolar properties of organic compounds such as oil affect the types of intermolecular attractions they can form. Water as we know is polar, and therefore it does not attract oil molecules. In this investigation, you will observe and experience some of the challenges faced by scientists who attempt to clean up oil spills. A successful cleanup protects our coastlines, wildlife, and ocean-dwelling organisms.

Materials

- Vegetable oil
- Cocoa powder
- 150 mL beaker or small plastic cup
- Spoon
- Glass bowl or a 1.0 L beaker
- Piece of cork
- Dish detergent
- Hot tap water
- Sand
- Shallow plastic pan
- Cotton balls
- Paper towels
- Eye dropper
- Feather(s)

Part 1: Procedure

1. Fill your glass bowl with water to 1 in from the top.

2. Measure 2/3 cup of vegetable oil (120 mL) and add it to your beaker. Now mix in 1 or 2 teaspoons of cocoa powder with the oil. This will make it look more like crude oil.

3. Pour your oil mixture into the bowl of water very slowly. If you pour too quickly, the experiment will not work as well.

4. What happens to the oil? Record your observations.

5. Place a piece of cork on the surface of the "oil spill," and then remove it. Record your observations.

6. Place the feather on the surface of the "oil spill," and then remove it. Record your observations

Part 2: Thinking about it

1. Describe what happened right at the beginning, when you added the oil to the water.

2. Explain what happened to the cork and to the feather when you placed them on the oil.

3. What do you think would happen if you shook a sample of water with vegetable oil and cocoa? This is similar to what happens when the wind, currents, and tides mix seawater containing oil.

Part 3: Cleaning up an oil spill

1. Using the shallow plastic pan, add some sand at one end to simulate a shoreline (beach). You may place a couple of rocks there too.
2. Slowly add water to your plastic pan using a large beaker.
3. Measure about a half cup of vegetable oil and mix in some cocoa powder for color.
4. Add the vegetable oil mixture to your plastic pan.
5. Have your group select two items from the cleanup materials available (cotton balls, paper towels, or eye dropper).
6. Test each material or item and record your results.
7. Add a few drops of liquid soap to the oil in your plastic pan. Record your observations.
8. Now try to clean up the spill some more using the same materials you used earlier.

Part 4: What happened?

a. How successfully were you able to clean up your oil spill?

b. Based on this experience, what would scientists need to consider when giving advice to cleanup crews after an oil spill?

c. Find out what materials are used to clean up a real oil spill. List a few here along with how they work.

Part 5: What did you learn?

a. What do you think happens to small amounts of oil that mix with the water? Explain.

b. Do you think crude oil is more or less dense than vegetable oil? Explain.

c. Suggest a way to clean off a seagull that has oil in its feathers.

d. Crude oil is damaging to our ocean and shoreline ecosystems. To have successful cleanups, we need to carefully consider its chemical properties. Give two examples of chemical properties that would be important to consider.

e. Based on your laboratory experiments, what effect does soap have on oil? Do your best to explain at the molecular level.

f. Predict two environmental concerns that would arise following an oil spill.

A NATURAL APPROACH TO
CHEMISTRY

17B: Distilling Aromatic Hydrocarbons

How are aromatic compounds isolated? What do they have in common?

Many of the "natural flavors" and "fragrances" that we find in food, perfumes, creams and other products come directly from natural products by a process called distillation. In this experiment, you will isolate some common fragrances and natural flavors using completely natural processes to create familiar smells using objects you can find in the kitchen or in the garden.

Materials

- Lab-Master with heater and condenser
- Crushed ice
- 250 mL beaker
- Plenty of salt
- 25 mm test tubes
- Stirring rod
- Mortar and pestle
- Pipettes

- Boiling chips or rocks
- One or more of the following spices: rose petals, vanilla beans, cloves, cinnamon, nutmeg, cardamom, anise, powdered or whole allspice, caraway seed, lemon peel, orange peel, turmeric, and cumin

Part 1: Setting up the experiment

1. Crush enough ice to fill a 250 mL beaker.

2. Fill a test tube 1/4 of the way with your spice. If your spice is powdered, just add it in. If it is whole, crush it first using the mortar and pestle.

3. Put 30 mL of hot water into the test tube. Drop a boiling chip or rock into the test tube. Stir your spice mixture well for 30 s.

4. Place the test tube into the heater.

5. Fill the cold side of the condenser with crushed ice. Pour salt over this crushed ice. Place the condenser on top of the test tube and heater apparatus.

6. Set your Lab-Master's heater to 125°C in **Heater Feedback** mode. Your setup should look like the picture on the right.

Part 2: Distilling your spice

1. Begin heating the spice–water mixture. Allow the mixture to come to a boil.

2. Notice how the spice mixture boils and how steam rises out of the test tube and is condensed in the condenser. This condensed steam is your distillate.

3. Continue distilling this mixture for 30 minutes. While distilling, watch the setup carefully. You will have to do two things to keep the mixture distilling properly:
   i. If the water level drops to 1/2 of its original level, add 15 mL of hot water.
   ii. If the ice in the condenser melts, remove the melted water with the pipette and then add more fresh crushed ice. Pour salt over this ice as before.

Part 3: Thinking about what you have learned

a. The Lab-Master can heat to 150°C. Why did we set it to 125°C? Why did we add a boiling chip? What could a very high temperature do to our aromatic compounds?

b. Why do we add salt to the ice?

c. Study the main aromatic compounds (essential oils) found in the spices used in this investigation. What similarities do you notice about all these molecules? What can you say about many aromatic compounds based on this similarity?

Spice	Molecule	Spice	Molecule
Allspice	*Eugenol*	Anise	*Anethole*
Cinnamon	*Cinnamaldehyde*	Cumin	*Cuminaldehyde*
Vanilla	*Vanillin*	Nutmeg	*Myristicin*
Caraway	*Carvone*	Turmeric	*Turmerone*

A NATURAL APPROACH TO
CHEMISTRY

18A: Analysis of Milk

What is in nonfat milk? How much food energy is in milk?

Did you ever wonder why milk is so nutritious? Almost all mammals consume milk when they are young. Milk contains different amounts of protein, carbohydrate, fat, and water. It also includes vitamins and antibodies that help young animals to grow. By taking advantage of the chemical properties of milk ingredients, we will determine the amounts of protein and water in a sample of milk.

Materials	
• 30.0 mL of nonfat milk	• 1.0 M HCl
• 100 mL beaker	• 3 mL pipette
• 250 mL beaker	• Filter paper
• Mass balance	• Small funnel
• 50 mL graduated cylinder	• 25 mm test tube
	• Microwave oven

We will separate the protein and water from a sample of nonfat milk. Since our sample contains no fat, the remaining portion of our sample will represent the amount of carbohydrate.

Part 1: Finding the amount of protein

1. Obtain a 100 mL beaker and measure its mass using the balance. Record the mass in Table 1 on the next page.

2. Measure 20.0 mL of nonfat milk into a graduated cylinder. Pour this milk into the 100 mL beaker and weigh it. Record your mass in Table 1.

3. Add about 2.0 mL of 1.0 M HCl one drop at a time. There will about 25 drops in a milliliter, so you will need about 50 drops total.

4. Mix the contents of the beaker by swirling, and allow it to sit for 3–5 minutes.

5. Place your initials near the top of the filter paper and weigh it to find its mass. Record the mass in Table 1. Fold the filter paper in half, then fold it in half again so that it is cone shaped. Place the filter paper in the funnel and open one fold. You want to have three folds on one side and one on the other. Wet the filter paper a little with some distilled water to make it stay in place.

6. After your milk sits for a few (3–5) minutes, pour it through the funnel. The coagulated part of the milk will be trapped by the filter paper. This is milk protein. Be sure to scrape out any remaining milk protein from the beaker into the filter. Then rinse your beaker with 3–5 mL of water and pour this into the filter. It will take some time for the liquid to run through the filter paper, so you need to be patient.

7. After the filtration is complete allow the filter paper and filtrate to dry completely.

8. Weigh and record the mass of the paper and the milk protein in Table 1.

139

Part 2: Finding the amount of water

1. Weigh an empty 250 mL glass beaker. Record the mass in Table 2 below.

2. Measure 6.0 mL of nonfat milk, add it to the beaker, and reweigh. Record the mass of your milk in Table 2.

3. Place the beaker in the microwave oven for 30 s time intervals at 50% power.

4. Heat the milk in the microwave oven for another 30 s at 50% power. Keep heating slowly and be patient, because it will take several repeated heatings to get the milk to lose most of its water. You must heat the milk gently! If you heat it too quickly, the milk will bubble out, spatter, and you will lose mass, which greatly affects your results.

5. Stop heating when the milk becomes thick and looks as though it is unchanged with heating.

6. Allow the beaker to cool and reweigh it. Record the mass in Table 2.

Table 1. Data for protein percentage calculation

Mass of beaker	Mass of beaker and milk	Mass of milk	Mass of filter paper	Mass of filter paper and protein	Mass of protein	% protein

Table 2. Data for water percentage calculation

Mass of beaker	Mass of beaker and milk	Mass of milk (before)	Mass of beaker and milk after heating	Mass of milk (after)	Mass of water	% water

140

Part 3: Finding the amount of carbohydrate

To find the amount of carbohydrate, we will need to calculate the percentage of protein in your sample from Part 1, and we will need to calculate the percentage of water in your sample from Part 2. We are assuming that, because we are using nonfat milk, we do not have to include fat content.

$$\% \text{ protein} = \frac{\text{mass of protein}}{\text{mass of milk}} \times 100$$

1. Follow the formula and plug in your data to obtain your percentage of protein from Table 1 and your percentage of water from Table 2.

$$\% \text{ water} = \frac{\text{mass of water}}{\text{mass of milk}} \times 100$$

2. To determine the amount of carbohydrate in your sample, you will need to add together your percent protein and percent water and subtract that sum from 100%:

$$100\% - (\% \text{ protein} + \% \text{ water}) = \% \text{ carbohydrate}$$

3. Record the amount of carbohydrate in your sample and compare it with that determined by another group.

Part 4: Determining the energy in nonfat milk

Proteins and carbohydrates provide the body with energy. The amount of energy provided by protein and carbohydrate is the same at about 4,000 cal/g or 4 Cal/g (where 1 Cal = 1 kcal = 1,000 cal). This means we will get the same amount of energy from burning carbohydrate or protein. Using your lab data and results for the percent protein and percent carbohydrate, we will determine the amount of chemical energy in one cup of milk. One cup of milk weighs approximately 250 g. Use Table 3 to help you determine the total number of calories in one cup of milk.

Table 3. Food Energy in one cup of milk

Mass of 1 cup of nonfat milk	Percent (%) converted to decimal	Mass of nutrient (g)	Energy value (Cal/g)	Total calories (energy)
250 g	_____ protein		4	
250 g	_____ carbohydrate		4	

a.   Complete the table using your laboratory results.

b.   Add up the total number of food calories (Cal) in your milk from protein and carbohydrate.

Part 5: What did you learn?

Table 4. Percent composition of nonfat milk

	Average values
% Protein	5.0%
% Carbohydrate	3.5%
% Water	90.8%
Total Cal/cup	80 Cal

1. Compare your laboratory values to the average values listed in Table 4. Write a few sentences that summarize your results.

2. Fat from whole milk provides 9 Cal/g compared to the 4 Cal/g in protein and carbohydrate. Suppose you used whole milk in your experiment and obtained the results in Table 5:

Table 5. Mass composition of whole milk

1 cup = 250 g	Mass of nutrient (g)	Energy (Cal/g)
Protein	9.0	4
Carbohydrate	12.0	4
Fat	7.0	9

3. How many Calories (Cal) are contained in the cup of whole milk from each source?

   • Protein Cal =

   • Carbohydrate Cal =

   • Fat Cal =

4. How many total Calories are in the cup of whole milk?

5. How do your Calorie values for whole milk and nonfat milk compare?

A NATURAL APPROACH TO
CHEMISTRY

18B: Catalysis and Enzymes

Do enzymes cause chemical change? What effect does temperature have on enzyme activity?

Enzymes are protein molecules that are responsible for catalyzing many different types of chemical reactions. In nature many metabolic processes depend upon enzyme molecules to make the reactions occur at a faster rate. In this investigation, you will investigate an enzyme in pineapple called bromelain. The gelatin contained in Jell-O™ is a gelling agent that makes the dessert hold its shape. Gelatin is made up of proteins that form collagen in the skin and bones of animals. The pineapple enzyme bromelain hydrolyzes the proteins in gelatin, causing them to break apart. The activity of this enzyme will affect the rate of the gelling process.

Materials

- Ten clear plastic cups or 150 mL beakers
- 1 qt glass jar or 1.0 L beaker
- 2 qt sauce pan or 2.0 L beaker
- Stirring rods or popsicle sticks
- 100 mL graduated cylinder or measuring cup
- 6 oz box of Jell-O® dessert (for 10 samples)
- Canned pineapple slices
- Fresh pineapple
- Sun-dried pineapple rings
- Mass balance
- Lab-Master with heater and temperature probe
- Spoons; small fork or tweezers

You need to be careful when transferring the hot pineapple and the boiling water! Be sure to use a potholder or an insulated glove. The samples cannot be eaten unless you have used utensils only used for cooking food and not for laboratory purposes. Sun-dried pineapple can be found at some health food stores.

Part 1: Procedure.

1. Measure 35 mL of tap water and place it in a test tube. Place the test tube in the Lab-Master and heat the water until it boils.

2. Measure out 16.0 g of gelatin and place it in a plastic cup or 150 mL beaker.

3. Using an insulated glove, carefully pour the boiling water into the cup containing the gelatin. Stir until the gelatin dissolves.

4. While stirring, add 40 mL of cold tap water to your cup.

5. Repeat steps 1–4 two more times. This will allow you to test three samples of pineapple.

6. Your instructor will assign two groups to make the "control," which includes steps 1–4 with *no* pineapple added. This will serve as a useful reference.

7. Next, cut a slice of canned pineapple into four equal pieces. Place one piece in one of your cups (or beakers) containing the gelatin. Label the cup containing the canned pineapple with your group's name.

8. Cut a slice of fresh pineapple about the same size as your canned pineapple. Place this in one of your cups (or beakers) containing the gelatin. Label the cup containing the fresh pineapple with your group's name.

9. Finally, add 25 mL of tap water to a large test tube for heating in your Lab-Master. Heat until it boils, using your temperature probe to record the temperature.

10. Cut a piece of fresh pineapple that will fit into your Lab-Master test tube. If necessary, cut two smaller pieces that roughly equal the amount used in your other trials.

11. Place a piece of fresh pineapple in the hot water in your test tube, and heat for the assigned amount of time. Your instructor will assign groups to heat for 0.5, 1.0, 1.5, and 2.0 min. You need to record the time your group is assigned in your lab notebook.

12. After your fresh pineapple has heated for the correct amount of time, use a small fork or tweezers to remove it and place it in the gelatin cup. Record your time and your group's name on the cup.

13. Place all of the samples in a cool place. If available, a refrigerator will help the gelling process.

14. Observe your samples the *next day* and record your final results.

Part 2: Gathering results

Gather your classmates' results and enter them into a table like Table 1.

Table 1: Class data for gelling experiment

Sample		Result
Control (no pineapple)		
Fresh pineapple		
Canned pineapple		
Sun dried pineapple		
	Time heated (min)	
Fresh pineapple	0.5	
Fresh pineapple	1.0	
Fresh pineapple	1.5	
Fresh pineapple	2.0	

Look over the results and write a few sentences describing them. Do they agree with each other? Explain.

Part 3: What did you learn?

a. What does the control prove? How is it useful in your experimental results? Explain.

b. In each of the types of pineapple you tested, was the activity of the bromelain enzyme similar? Explain.

c. What happens at the molecular level when the enzyme "hydrolyzes" the gelatin proteins? A simple explanation will suffice.

d. Perform an Internet search on the "structure of gelatin" and find out the common amino acids in gelatin. List them here.

e. What type of protein structure is responsible for the "gelling" caused by gelatin? (Hint: What is the picture above?)

f. How was the enzyme affected by heat in your experiment? Explain.

18C: Building an Amino Acid Chain

How are amino acid molecules connected to form a protein? What type of chemical bond joins amino acids together?

Proteins are required for almost all chemical reactions that take place in our bodies, and they are formed from amino acids. In this investigation, we will build amino acid molecules and connect them together to form a chain. Our protein chain will have eight amino acids along with a start and stop sequence. Real proteins are at least 100 amino acids long! We will also "read," or decode, what the amino acid sequence is and determine what it "says."

Materials

- Molecular modeling set
- Amino acid chart (see p. 586 of textbook or handout)

Proteins are produced during the process of translation. Translation takes place using a type of RNA called messenger RNA, because it carries the message of what type of protein sequence to make. Messenger RNA gets its "directions" from DNA. DNA is where the genetic code for protein synthesis comes from, but the directions are carried by the messenger RNA to the place where the proteins are made.

Part 1: Assembling amino acids

The amino acids you will assemble are: valine, leucine, asparagine, aspartic acid, glycine, alanine, serine, and cysteine. The start sequence is ATG, and the stop sequence is TAG.

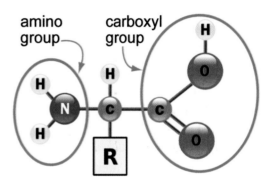

1. Build four different amino acids in your group of four students.
2. Now two groups can join up so that together you will have eight amino acids.

Part 2: Building a protein chain

3. Connect your amino acids, forming peptide bonds as shown below. Follow the sequence: start/valine/serine/cystine/asparagine/glycine/alanine/serine/alanine/valine/aspartic acid /leucine/flycine/aspartic acid/stop. One water molecule is removed for each peptide bond formed.

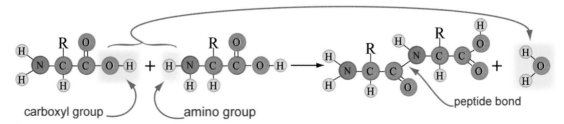

4. Record the name of each amino acid as it is joined, so that you can check the "sequence" of the chain that is forming.
5. Each person takes a turn adding their amino acid to the chain and forming a peptide bond.
6. Continue until the sequence is finished. Several groups may have made the sequence. It should be the same, if it is bonded correctly.

Part 3: Understanding an amino acid sequence

The names of the amino acids you made are specified by three codons. Codons are made up of a sequence of three of the four nitrogenous bases: A (adenine), G (guanine), U (uracil), and C (cytosine). A codon sequence carried by RNA "spells" the amino acid sequence.

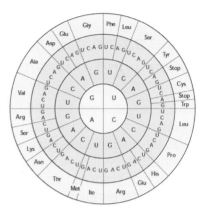

Read the wheel from inside to outside

1. Compare the following codon sequence to your amino acid chain sequence.
   AUG/GUG/AGC/UGC/GAC/GGC/GCA/AGC/GCA/GUG/
   AAC/CUA/GGC/AAC/UAG.
   Use the wheel shown to help you.

2. How does your amino acid chain compare to this sequence? Explain.

Part 4: Thinking about it

1. Look carefully at the amino acids that were used to make the protein. See if you can determine whether they are acidic, basic, or neutral amino acids.

2. What you have made is called the *primary structure* of a protein. The primary structure dictates how the amino acid folds and/or coils to take its shape. What intermolecular forces are responsible for the tertiary structure of a protein?

3. The side chains play an important role in protein chemistry. How would you predict the polar amino acids to orient themselves in an aqueous environment, like that in our bodies?

4. In contrast, how would you predict the nonpolar amino acids to orient themselves?

5. Look carefully at the protein chain constructed by your class. Can you imagine that proteins are made up of a minimum of 100 amino acids? Think about what this must mean at the molecular level. Write down a few of your thoughts about this.

6. What does it mean when the genetic code is said to be "degenerate?"

7. How do proteins "facilitate" chemical reactions? What can they do?

8. By studying the fossil record, scientists have observed changes in amino acids over time. These observations have led to the theory of the "molecular clock." This theory is used to classify organisms and establish relations among them. Do some research on this topic and answer the following questions:

   a. What is the scientific basis for the theory of the molecular clock?

   b. What are the limitations of this theory?

   c. Is the theory of the molecular clock well accepted by scientists?

   d. What does the theory of the molecular clock tell you about the scientific process?

19A: The Water Cycle

Where does the water we drink come from? How do water molecules cycle around Earth?

The water here on Earth has been around since the very beginning, roughly 4.5 billion years ago. When you drink a glass of water, stop and consider the fact that the water molecules you are drinking have been "recycled" for a very long time. A water molecule that you drink may have been the same one that a dinosaur drank! In this investigation, we will observe the physical changes of water and see firsthand how it is recycled. Water's ability to undergo these changes is responsible for the Earth's ability to sustain life.

Materials

- Lab-Master with temperature probe, heater, and condenser apparatus
- Crushed ice
- 25 mm test tube
- 50 mL beaker or test tube for condensate collection
- Muddy water

Part 1: Setting up

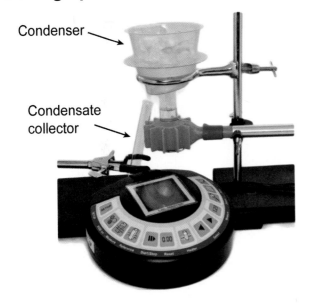

Condenser

Condensate collector

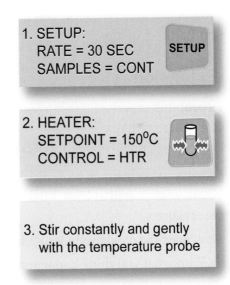

1. SETUP:
   RATE = 30 SEC   **SETUP**
   SAMPLES = CONT

2. HEATER:
   SETPOINT = 150°C
   CONTROL = HTR

3. Stir constantly and gently with the temperature probe

Part 2: Melting ice

1. Fill a test tube about half full of crushed ice. Add some water until the test tube is about 2/3 of the way full.

2. In the SETUP mode, set the RATE to 30 SEC and the SAMPLES to CONT (continuous). This will take a temperature measurement every 30 s for as long as you are heating the water.

3. Stir gently with the temperature probe. Press **Start/Stop** to start taking data and record the temperature of the ice water in your lab notebook. This is the temperature at "0 minutes."

4. Set the heater to 150°C.

5. Stir the test tube *constantly* but *gently* with the temperature probe.

6. Watch carefully and note the time and temperature when all the ice has melted.

7. Continue to heat the water and begin Part 3.

Part 3: Boiling and condensing water vapor

1. Place the condenser apparatus on top of the test tube as the water continues to heat.
2. Fill the top of the condenser with ice and place a small test tube or beaker under the condenser to collect the condensate.
3. Continue to heat the water to boiling until about half of it has vaporized.
4. Turn the Lab-Master's heater off.

Part 4: Thinking about what you observed

a. What happened to the ice as you added heat? Be sure to explain your answer at the molecular level. In other words, what changes occurred that affected the ice molecules?

b. Can you think of a similar example of the water cycle in our environment?

c. What happened to the water as it continued to warm up? Once again, explain this at the molecular level. In other words, what effect does heat have on the water molecules?

d. Near the equator the surface temperature of the ocean gets warm, and this is why people like to vacation in this area. What do you think happens to these surface water molecules in warm regions here on Earth? Explain.

Part 5: Extension

1. Repeat this experiment using some muddy water. Fill your test tube about halfway with the mud and water mixture.
2. Set your heater to 150°C and begin heating.
3. As your water starts to boil, place the condenser apparatus over the top of the test tube. Heat until you have collected at least 3.0 mL of water. You need enough volume to allow you to make good observations.
4. How does the condensate look? Is it muddy?
5. Explain what you think happened in this experiment. Be specific and focus on using the word "molecule(s)" in your explanation.

Part 6: Making connections

a. Where does most of the groundwater supply on land come from? Explain in a couple of sentences.

b. The water molecule aids in the warming of our atmosphere. When liquid water is converted to water vapor, energy is absorbed. Can you guess what happens to the amount of water vapor in our air as the surface temperatures here on Earth rise? Explain your thinking.

c. The amount of water vapor in our atmosphere actually amplifies the "greenhouse effect." In terms of your experiment, think about how the addition of more water molecules in the atmosphere would affect the overall water cycle.

d. Why might we experience more frequent storms as a result of the global warming process? Explain.

A NATURAL APPROACH TO
CHEMISTRY

19B: Ocean Currents

How do ocean currents work? What effects do salinity and temperature have on the density of ocean water?

You may already know that the ocean currents play an important role in regulating our climate around the world. Ocean currents are put in motion by density differences in the ocean waters. In this investigation, you will be able to see for yourself how temperature and salt concentration both affect the density of water. You will also see how these differences in density cause water to rise or sink. The fact that water sinks when it is more dense explains what initiates the movement of ocean currents.

Materials

- Two 12 oz clear plastic cups or two 250 mL glass beakers
- 100 mL beaker
- Salt
- 250 mL of salt water
- Ice cubes and tap water
- Blue food coloring
- NaCl (salt)
- Two spoons
- 1.0 L glass beaker or large glass jar
- Lab-Master with temperature probe

Part 1: Investigating the density of fresh water and salt water

1. Label your plastic cups or beakers as fresh and salt water.
2. Fill the beakers with room temperature tap water and room temperature salt water. Place an ice cube gently into the beaker of fresh water using the spoon.
3. Add 2 or 3 drops of food coloring on top of the ice cube. Record your observations.
4. Next, gently place an ice cube in the salt water.
5. Add 2 or 3 drops of food coloring on top of the ice cube. Record your observations.

Part 2: Thinking about it

1. In which beaker did the ice cube melt the fastest?
2. Describe in a couple of sentences what you observed when the ice cube melted in the fresh water cup. Include what happened to the food coloring in your description.
3. Describe in a couple of sentences what you observed when the ice cube melted in the salt water cup. Include what happened to the food coloring in your description.
4. Do you think fresh water or salt water is more dense? Explain your reasoning.

Part 3: Density and temperature

1. Fill a 250 mL beaker a little more than halfway with room temperature water.

2. Measure about 50 mL of the salt water at room temperature in a graduated cylinder. Add a few drops of food coloring until it is deeply colored. Mix.

3. Slowly pour the salt water into the 250 mL fresh water beaker. Record your observations.

4. Fill a large 1.0 L beaker or a glass bowl about 3/4 of the way up with room temperature water. Measure and record the temperature of your water.

5. Add about 50 mL of tap water in a 100 mL beaker or cup. Mix in 1 heaping teaspoon of table salt [NaCl(s)] until it dissolves.

6. Place your temperature probe into the salt water and measure the temperature.

7. Add 3 or 4 ice cubes to the salty tap water. Stir the ice and record the coldest temperature after the ice has finished melting. The water needs to be cold; add ice cubes to lower the temperature.

8. Add 5 drops of food coloring to your cold salty water. Swirl to mix.

9. Slowly add the cold salty water to your room temperature water. Record your observations.

Part 4: What happened?

1. In both cases, what happened to the salty water? Why do you think this happened?

2. Did the temperature of the salt water make any difference in its behavior? Explain.

3. What do you think would happen if the water had more salt in it?

4. What would you expect to happen if you made the salt water 20°C colder than the room temperature water?

Part 5: What did you learn?

a. What do you think happens to ocean water when it arrives at the north pole? Explain.

b. What do you think happens to ocean water as it is warmed by the Sun near the equator? Explain.

c. Ocean water contains a large amount of salt. As water freezes and forms ice crystals, the salt ions are pushed out of the ice crystal structure and left behind in the remaining water. How do you think this affects the density of the water? What effect might this have on the ocean?

d. Look at the picture to the right and write a few sentences about what you think is happening.

e. Based on your laboratory experiments, how do you think the increased temperature caused by global warming will affect the ocean currents?

20A: Half-Life Experiment: Coin Toss

What is a half-life? How can we simulate this without using radiation?

Radioactive elements decay with a certain time constant. This means that each radioactive atom has a certain probability of decaying in a given time. This leads to a "half-life," or a time after which half of the original element will remain. In this investigation, you will simulate a radioactive element using pennies instead of radiation.

Materials

- A large number of pennies
- Graph paper

Part 1: Simulating half-life: Short version

This experiment is quite simple. It only involves flipping coins and graphing the results.

1. Start with 10 pennies. Call this "$t = 0$" on your graph, and plot a "10" on the y axis.
2. Toss all 10 pennies on the ground or on the table. Remove all pennies that turn up tails. These will be the decayed atoms.
3. Count the remaining pennies and plot the number. This point will be at "$t = 1$" on the x axis.
4. Repeat Steps 2 and 3. Plot this at "$t = 2$" on the x axis.
5. Repeat Steps 2 and 3 until all the pennies have "decayed."

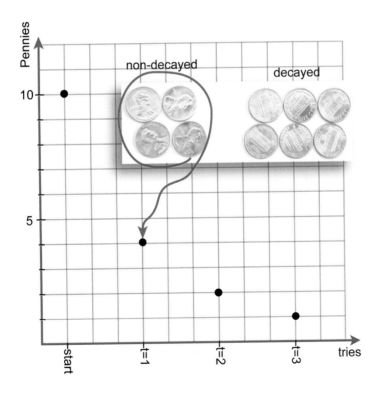

Part 2: Simulating half-life: Long version of Part 1

Repeat the experiment from Part 1, except use 100 pennies. Continue running it until all the pennies "decay."

Part 3: Simulating half-life: Long version of Part 2

1. Repeat the experiment from Part 1, using only 10 pennies.

2. Now repeat this experiment a total of 10 times. Add the data from each of the 10 experiments, and plot this on a new graph.

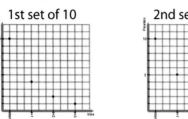 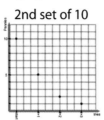 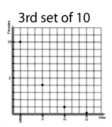 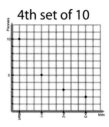

1st set of 10   2nd set of 10   3rd set of 10   4th set of 10

Continue up to 10th set of 10 pennies.
Record the data for each try. Add total
non-decayed per try and record on the table

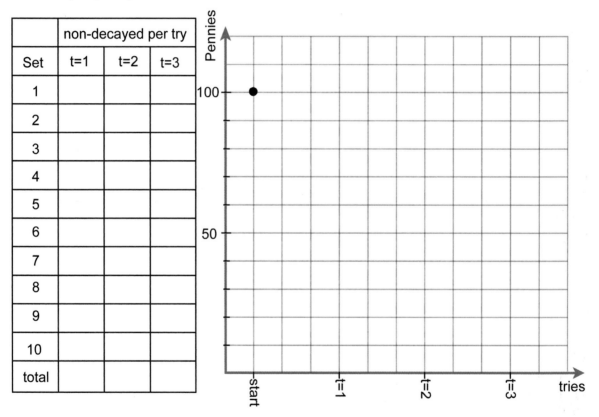

Set	non-decayed per try		
---	t=1	t=2	t=3
1			
2			
3			
4			
5			
6			
7			
8			
9			
10			
total			

Part 4: Thinking about what you have learned

1. How smooth is the graph from Part 1? How about Part 2? How about Part 3?

2. What similarities do you notice about the graphs from Parts 2 and Part 3? Why is that?

3. How would you make this experiment even more precise?

Part 2 and Part 3 make an interesting point about half-life. You should notice that the graphs end up being very similar. Running 10 experiments with 10 pennies each is *exactly the same* as running one half-life experiment with 100 pennies. This is because half-life is only dependent on the *type* of atom present. It has nothing to do with how many atoms there are, how close they are to each other, what time it is, or any other variables. It shows that no matter how many radioactive atoms you have, half will decay after the half-life.

A NATURAL APPROACH TO
CHEMISTRY

20B: The Alchemical Race

How can one element change into another?

Ancient chemists were obsessed with trying to turn lead into gold. They realized over and over again that it was impossible to do in their lab. What they didn't realize is that it *is* possible for one element to change into another, not through alchemy, but through radioactive decay! In this lab you will play a game where you try to reach a stable nucleus first through random radioactive decays, simulated by rolling dice.

Materials
- Chart of radioactive decay chains (available at ANaturalApproachtoChemistry.com)
- One blue six-sided dice
- One green six-sided dice
- One 30-s hourglass or Lab-Master

Part 1: The rules

a. Each game is divided into several rounds. The object of each round is to reach your stable target element first. The player who wins the most rounds at the end of the lab period wins the game.

b. At the start of each round, each player rolls two dice to see which nuclei he or she gets. Look up what nuclei you got on the next page. If you get a dice combination that is not shown on the table of the next page you must roll your dice again.

c. Then each player rolls the dice to see who goes first. The player who rolls the highest number gets to try to decay first.

d. Players then take turns rolling one die to simulate a radioactive decay process. The chart on the right tells you how your nucleus can decay based on your roll.

e. You then have 30 s to decide if or how your nucleus can decay. One of the following four things can happen:

1. If you roll a "no decay," then you lose a turn.

2. If you roll a decay process that your nucleus can undergo, you must say the parent nucleus, the decay process, the energy released, and the daughter nucleus out loud.

3. If you roll a decay process that your nucleus cannot undergo, then you lose a turn.

4. If you take more than 30 s to decide what to do, then you lose a turn.

f. The first player to reach his or her stable nucleus wins that round.

Alpha decay — helium

Beta decay — electron

Gamma decay and electron capture — electron, photon

Proton decay — proton

Beta and neutron decay — neutron, electron

No decay

Part 2: The nuclides

Use the chart here at the start of the round to see which starting and ending nuclei you got.

Dice (Blue, Green)	Start	End	Dice (Blue, Green)	Start	End
(1, 1)	$^{145}_{63}Eu$	$^{145}_{60}Nd$	(3, 1)	$^{32}_{11}Na$	$^{30}_{14}Si$
(1, 2)	$^{145}_{57}La$	$^{145}_{60}Nd$	(3, 2)	$^{205}_{84}Po$	$^{201}_{80}Hg$
(1, 3)	$^{47}_{17}Ci$	$^{46}_{20}Ca$	(3, 3)	$^{150}_{65}Tb$	$^{142}_{60}Nd$
(1, 4)	$^{190}_{79}Au$	$^{182}_{74}W$	(3, 4)	$^{171}_{67}Ho$	$^{171}_{70}Tm$
(1, 5)	$^{39}_{16}S$	$^{39}_{19}K$	(3, 5)	$^{20}_{6}C$	$^{19}_{9}F$
(1, 6)	$^{246}_{95}Am$	$^{238}_{42}U$	(3, 6)	$^{62}_{31}Ga$	$^{62}_{28}Ni$
(2, 1)	$^{51}_{19}K$	$^{50}_{22}Ti$	(4, 1)	$^{143}_{55}Cs$	$^{142}_{58}Ce$
(2, 2)	$^{132}_{59}Pr$	$^{131}_{56}Ba$	(4, 2)	$^{24}_{8}O$	$^{23}_{11}Na$
(2, 3)	$^{243}_{98}Cf$	$^{239}_{94}Pu$	(4, 3)	$^{214}_{85}At$	$^{206}_{82}Pb$
(2, 4)	$^{43}_{16}S$	$^{42}_{19}K$	(4, 4)	$^{51}_{20}Ca$	$^{51}_{23}V$
(2, 5)	$^{175}_{79}Au$	$^{170}_{75}Re$	(4, 5)	$^{161}_{73}Ta$	$^{153}_{68}Er$
(2, 6)	$^{69}_{28}Ni$	$^{69}_{31}Ga$	(4, 6)	$^{44}_{25}Mn$	$^{42}_{21}Sc$

21A: Astronomical Spectroscopy

How is spectroscopy used in astronomy? What can it tell us?

We have already seen how spectroscopy can help us identify elements, or even identify compounds with multiple elements. Spectroscopy can also be used to tell us many things about the universe around us. We can learn about the composition of distant stars, determine the approximate age of stars, and even analyze what compounds exist on faraway planets. Spectroscopy is helping us to determine whether life can exist in outer space! In this investigation, you will learn how spectroscopy is used in astronomy.

<table>
<tr><td>Materials</td></tr>
<tr><td>• Element spectroscopy cards
  (1 set per group)</td></tr>
<tr><td>• Star spectroscopy cards
  (1 set per group)</td></tr>
</table>

Part 1: The elemental composition of stars

a. Look at the element spectroscopy cards. Notice that they are *emission* cards, that is, they show the colors that those elements *emit* when they are excited. What creates these emission lines?

b. Now look at the astronomical spectroscopy cards. Notice that they are *absorption* cards, that is, they show which wavelengths of light are *absorbed* in the star. This is because the hot plasma in stars emits all wavelengths of light, and the elements in the star *absorb the same* characteristic wavelengths of light. (Remember your experiments with the Lab-Master spectrophotometer?) The star produces all wavelengths of light in its core from fusion. Where in the star is its absorption spectrum created?

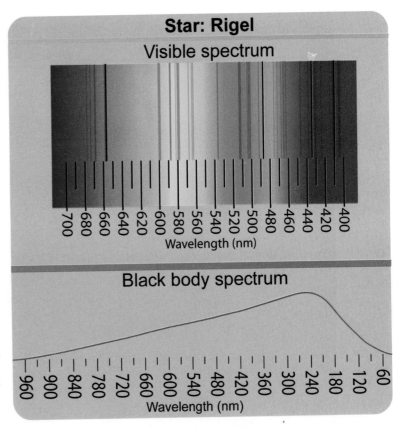

c. Compare the element cards to the star cards. What similarities do you notice?

d. Determine which elements are present in each star by matching the *emission* lines on the element cards to the *absorption* lines on the star cards.

e. As stars burn, they convert lighter elements to heavier ones by nuclear fusion. Rank the stars on the star cards from youngest to oldest based on this information.

f. Notice that some elements are half-shaded in. What do you suppose this means in terms of the amount of that element in the star?

Part 2: The temperatures of stars

a.   Notice that each star spectroscopy card also has a "blackbody spectrum." This spectrum shows the intensities of each color of light coming from each star.

b.   What temperature corresponds to the hottest stars? What temperature corresponds to the coldest stars?

c.   Rank the stars from hottest to coldest.

d.   What similarity do you notice between your two lists? Why do you suppose that is?

e.   One star should not fit this pattern. Which one is it? Research online why this star is different from the others. You should find some interesting information about what this star will be doing very soon.

f.   (Optional) The graph below is called the Hertzsprung–Russell (HR) diagram. Do some research online about this diagram and about the stars we have studied in this investigation. Place Rigel and the other stars on the diagram. Which of the stars that you studied is the hottest?

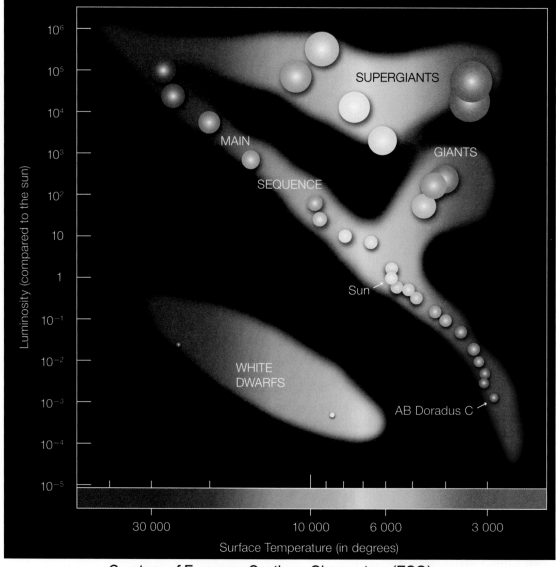

Courtesy of European Southern Observatory (ESO)

Table of the Elements

Element Name	Symbol	Atomic Number	Atomic Mass
Actinium	Ac	89	[227]
Aluminum	Al	13	26.98
Americium	Am	95	[243]
Antimony	Sb	51	121.76
Argon	Ar	18	39.95
Arsenic	As	33	74.92
Astatine	At	85	[210]
Barium	Ba	56	137.33
Berkelium	Bk	97	[247]
Beryllium	Be	4	9.01
Bismuth	Bi	83	208.98
Bohrium	Bh	107	[264]
Boron	B	5	10.81
Bromine	Br	35	79.90
Cadmium	Cd	48	112.41
Calcium	Ca	20	40.08
Californium	Cf	98	[251]
Carbon	C	6	12.01
Cerium	Ce	58	140.12
Cesium	Cs	55	132.91
Chlorine	Cl	17	35.45
Chromium	Cr	24	52.00
Cobalt	Co	27	58.93
Copper	Cu	29	63.55
Curium	Cm	96	[247]
Darmstadtium	Ds	110	[271]
Dubnium	Db	105	[262]
Dysprosium	Dy	66	162.50
Einsteinium	Es	99	[252]
Erbium	Er	68	167.26
Europium	Eu	63	151.96
Fermium	Fm	100	[257]
Fluorine	F	9	19.00
Francium	Fr	87	[223]
Gadolinium	Gd	64	157.25
Gallium	Ga	31	69.72
Germanium	Ge	32	72.61
Gold	Au	79	196.97
Hafnium	Hf	72	178.49
Hassium	Hs	108	[277]
Helium	He	2	4.00
Holmium	Ho	67	164.93
Hydrogen	H	1	1.01
Indium	In	49	114.82
Iodine	I	53	126.90
Iridium	Ir	77	192.22
Iron	Fe	26	55.85
Krypton	Kr	36	83.80
Lanthanum	La	57	138.91
Lawrencium	Lr	103	[262]
Lead	Pb	82	207.20
Lithium	Li	3	6.94
Lutetium	Lu	71	174.97
Magnesium	Mg	12	24.31
Manganese	Mn	25	54.94
Meitnerium	Mt	109	[268]
Mendelevium	Md	101	[258]
Mercury	Hg	80	200.59
Molybdenum	Mo	42	95.94

Element Name	Symbol	Atomic Number	Atomic Mass
Neodymium	Nd	60	144.24
Neon	Ne	10	20.18
Neptunium	Np	93	[237]
Nickel	Ni	28	58.69
Niobium	Nb	41	92.91
Nitrogen	N	7	14.01
Nobelium	No	102	[259]
Osmium	Os	76	190.23
Oxygen	O	8	16.00
Palladium	Pd	46	106.42
Phosphorus	P	15	30.97
Platinum	Pt	78	195.08
Plutonium	Pu	94	[244]
Polonium	Po	84	[210]
Potassium	K	19	39.10
Praseodymium	Pr	59	140.91
Promethium	Pm	61	[145]
Protactinium	Pa	91	231.04
Radium	Ra	88	[226]
Radon	Rn	86	[220]
Rhenium	Re	75	186.21
Rhodium	Rh	45	102.91
Roentgenium	Rg	111	[272]
Rubidium	Rb	37	85.47
Ruthenium	Ru	44	101.07
Rutherfordium	Rf	104	[261]
Samarium	Sm	62	150.36
Scandium	Sc	21	44.96
Seaborgium	Sg	106	[266]
Selenium	Se	34	78.96
Silicon	Si	14	28.09
Silver	Ag	47	107.87
Sodium	Na	11	22.99
Strontium	Sr	38	87.62
Sulfur	S	16	32.07
Tantalum	Ta	73	180.95
Technetium	Tc	43	[98]
Tellurium	Te	52	127.60
Terbium	Tb	65	158.93
Thallium	Tl	81	204.38
Thorium	Th	90	232.04
Thulium	Tm	69	168.93
Tin	Sn	50	118.71
Titanium	Ti	22	47.87
Tungsten	W	74	183.84
Ununbium	Uub	112	[285]
Ununhexium	Uuh	116	[292]
Ununoctium	Uuo	118	[294]
Ununpentium	Uup	115	[288]
Ununquadium	Uuq	114	[289]
Ununseptium	Uus	117	[293]
Ununtrium	Uut	113	[284]
Uranium	U	92	238.03
Vanadium	V	23	50.94
Xenon	Xe	54	131.29
Ytterbium	Yb	70	173.06
Yttrium	Y	39	88.91
Zinc	Zn	30	65.41
Zirconium	Zr	40	91.22

A value in square brackets is the atomic mass of the most stable isotope.

A NATURAL APPROACH TO CHEMISTRY

Periodic Table Colored by Element Groups

metals
- alkali metals
- alkaline earth metals
- transition metals
- rare earth metals
- other metals

nonmetals
- halogens
- noble gases
- other nonmetals

metalloids
- metalloids

Key

1	Atomic number
H	Symbol
1.0079	Atomic mass
hydrogen	Name

group 1 1A	group 2 2A	group 3 3B	group 4 4B	group 5 5B	group 6 6B	group 7 7B	group 8 8B	group 9 8B	group 10 8B	group 11 1B	group 12 2B	group 13 3A	group 14 4A	group 15 5A	group 16 6A	group 17 7A	group 18 8A
1 H 1.0079 hydrogen																	2 He 4.0028 helium
3 Li 6.941 lithium	4 Be 9.0122 beryllium											5 B 10.811 boron	6 C 12.011 carbon	7 N 14.007 nitrogen	8 O 15.999 oxygen	9 F 18.998 fluorine	10 Ne 20.180 neon
11 Na 22.990 sodium	12 Mg 24.305 magnesium											13 Al 26.982 aluminum	14 Si 28.086 silicon	15 P 30.974 phosphorous	16 S 32.065 sulfur	17 Cl 35.453 chlorine	18 Ar 39.948 argon
19 K 39.098 potassium	20 Ca 40.078 calcium	21 Sc 44.956 scandium	22 Ti 47.867 titanium	23 V 50.942 vanadium	24 Cr 51.996 chromium	25 Mn 54.938 manganese	26 Fe 55.845 iron	27 Co 58.933 cobalt	28 Ni 58.693 nickel	29 Cu 63.546 copper	30 Zn 65.38 zinc	31 Ga 69.723 gallium	32 Ge 72.61 germanium	33 As 79.922 arsenic	34 Se 78.96 selenium	35 Br 79.904 bromine	36 Kr 83.80 krypton
37 Rb 85.468 rubidium	38 Sr 87.62 strontium	39 Y 88.906 yttrium	40 Zr 91.224 zirconium	41 Nb 92.906 niobium	42 Mo 95.96 molybdenum	43 Tc (98) technetium	44 Ru 101.07 ruthenium	45 Rh 102.91 rhodium	46 Pd 106.42 palladium	47 Ag 107.87 silver	48 Cd 112.41 cadmium	49 In 114.82 indium	50 Sn 118.71 tin	51 Sb 121.76 antimony	52 Te 127.60 tellurium	53 I 126.90 iodine	54 Xe 131.29 xenon
55 Cs 132.91 cesium	56 Ba 137.33 barium	71 Lu 174.97 lutetium	72 Hf 178.49 hafnium	73 Ta 180.95 tantalum	74 W 183.84 tungsten	75 Re 186.21 rhenium	76 Os 190.23 osmium	77 Ir 192.22 iridium	78 Pt 195.08 platinum	79 Au 196.97 gold	80 Hg 200.559 mercury	81 Tl 204.38 thallium	82 Pb 207.2 lead	83 Bi 208.98 bismuth	84 Po (209) polonium	85 At (210) astatine	86 Rn (222) radon
87 Fr (223) francium	88 Ra (226) radium	103 Lr (262) lawrencium	104 Rf (267) rutherfordium	105 Db (268) dubnium	106 Sg (271) seaborgium	107 Bh (272) bohrium	108 Hs (270) hassium	109 Mt (276) meitnerium	110 Ds (281) darmstadtium	111 Rg (280) roentgenium	112 Uub (285) unumbium	113 Uut (284) ununtrium	114 Uuq (289) ununquadium	115 Uup (288) ununpentium	116 Uuh (293) ununhexium		118 Uuo (294) ununoctium

57 La 138.91 lanthanum	58 Ce 140.12 cerium	59 Pr 140.91 praseodymium	60 Nd 144.24 neodymium	61 Pm (145) promethium	62 Sm 150.36 samarium	63 Eu 151.96 europium	64 Gd 157.25 gadolinium	65 Tb 158.93 terbium	66 Dy 162.50 dysprosium	67 Ho 164.93 holmium	68 Er 167.26 erbium	69 Tm 168.93 thulium	70 Yb 173.06 ytterbium
89 Ac (227) actinium	90 Th 232.04 thorium	91 Pa 231.04 protactinium	92 U 238.03 uranium	93 Np (237) neptunium	94 Pu (244) plutonium	95 Am (243) americium	96 Cm (247) curium	97 Bk (247) berkelium	98 Cf (251) californium	99 Es (252) einsteinium	100 Fm (257) fermium	101 Md (258) mendelevium	102 No (259) nobelium

Valence electrons

1A	2A												3A	4A	5A	6A	7A	8A

Main group elements

Transition metals
(valence electrons vary)

3B 4B 5B 6B 7B ⟨ 8B ⟩ **1B 2B**

| 1 H 1.0079 hydrogen | | | | | | | | | | | | | | | | | | 2 He 4.0028 helium |

1 2 3 4 5 6 7 8

Period 1:
- **1 H** 1.0079 hydrogen
- **2 He** 4.0028 helium

Period 2:
- **3 Li** 6.941 lithium
- **4 Be** 9.0122 beryllium
- **5 B** 10.811 boron
- **6 C** 12.011 carbon
- **7 N** 14.007 nitrogen
- **8 O** 15.999 oxygen
- **9 F** 18.998 fluorine
- **10 Ne** 20.180 neon

Period 3:
- **11 Na** 22.990 sodium
- **12 Mg** 24.305 magnesium
- **13 Al** 26.982 aluminum
- **14 Si** 28.086 silicon
- **15 P** 30.974 phosphorous
- **16 S** 32.065 sulfur
- **17 Cl** 35.453 chlorine
- **18 Ar** 39.948 argon

Period 4:
- **19 K** 39.098 potassium
- **20 Ca** 40.078 calcium
- **21 Sc** 44.956 scandium
- **22 Ti** 47.867 titanium
- **23 V** 50.942 vanadium
- **24 Cr** 51.996 chromium
- **25 Mn** 54.938 manganese
- **26 Fe** 55.845 iron
- **27 Co** 58.933 cobalt
- **28 Ni** 58.693 nickel
- **29 Cu** 63.546 copper
- **30 Zn** 65.38 zinc
- **31 Ga** 69.723 gallium
- **32 Ge** 72.61 germanium
- **33 As** 79.922 arsenic
- **34 Se** 78.96 selenium
- **35 Br** 79.904 bromine
- **36 Kr** 83.80 krypton

Period 5:
- **37 Rb** 85.468 rubidium
- **38 Sr** 87.62 strontium
- **39 Y** 88.906 yttrium
- **40 Zr** 91.224 zirconium
- **41 Nb** 92.906 niobium
- **42 Mo** 95.96 molybdenum
- **43 Tc** (98) technetium
- **44 Ru** 101.07 ruthenium
- **45 Rh** 102.91 rhodium
- **46 Pd** 106.42 palladium
- **47 Ag** 107.87 silver
- **48 Cd** 112.41 cadmium
- **49 In** 114.82 indium
- **50 Sn** 118.71 tin
- **51 Sb** 121.76 antimony
- **52 Te** 127.60 tellurium
- **53 I** 126.90 iodine
- **54 Xe** 131.29 xenon

Period 6:
- **55 Cs** 132.91 cesium
- **56 Ba** 137.33 barium
- **71 Lu** 174.97 lutetium
- **72 Hf** 178.49 hafnium
- **73 Ta** 180.95 tantalum
- **74 W** 183.84 tungsten
- **75 Re** 186.21 rhenium
- **76 Os** 190.23 osmium
- **77 Ir** 192.22 iridium
- **78 Pt** 195.08 platinum
- **79 Au** 196.97 gold
- **80 Hg** 200.559 mercury
- **81 Tl** 204.38 thallium
- **82 Pb** 207.2 lead
- **83 Bi** 208.98 bismuth
- **84 Po** (209) polonium
- **85 At** (210) astatine
- **86 Rn** (222) radon

A Natural Approach to CHEMISTRY

Appendix A: Table of the Elements and Periodic Tables

A Natural Approach to Chemistry

Electronegativity — Na 0.93 sodium

low — high

group 1	group 2	group 3	group 4	group 5	group 6	group 7	group 8	group 9	group 10	group 11	group 12	group 13	group 14	group 15	group 16	group 17	group 18
H 2.1 hydrogen																	He --- helium
Li 0.98 lithium	Be 1.57 beryllium											B 2.04 boron	C 2.55 carbon	N 3.04 nitrogen	O 3.44 oxygen	F 3.98 fluorine	Ne --- neon
Na 0.93 sodium	Mg 1.31 magnesium											Al 1.61 aluminum	Si 1.9 silicon	P 2.19 phosphorous	S 2.58 sulfur	Cl 3.16 chlorine	Ar --- argon
K 0.82 potassium	Ca 1.0 calcium	Sc 1.36 scandium	Ti 1.54 titanium	V 1.63 vanadium	Cr 1.66 chromium	Mn 1.55 manganese	Fe 1.83 iron	Co 1.88 cobalt	Ni 1.91 nickel	Cu 1.9 copper	Zn 1.65 zinc	Ga 1.81 gallium	Ge 2.01 germanium	As 2.18 arsenic	Se 2.55 selenium	Br 2.96 bromine	Kr 3.0 krypton
Rb 0.82 rubidium	Sr 0.95 strontium	Y 1.22 yttrium	Zr 1.33 zirconium	Nb 1.6 niobium	Mo 2.16 molybdenum	Tc 1.9 technetium	Ru 2.2 ruthenium	Rh 2.28 rhodium	Pd 2.2 palladium	Ag 1.93 silver	Cd 1.69 cadmium	In 1.78 indium	Sn 1.96 tin	Sb 2.05 antimony	Te 2.1 tellurium	I 2.66 iodine	Xe 3.0 xenon
Cs 0.79 cesium	Ba 0.89 barium	Lu 1.27 lutetium	Hf 1.3 hafnium	Ta 1.5 tantalum	W 2.36 tungsten	Re 1.9 rhenium	Os 2.2 osmium	Ir 2.2 iridium	Pt 2.28 platinum	Au 2.54 gold	Hg 2.0 mercury	Tl 2.04 thallium	Pb 2.33 lead	Bi 2.02 bismuth	Po 2.0 polonium	At 2.2 astatine	Rn --- radon
Fr 0.7 francium	Ra 0.89 radium	Lr --- lawrencium	Rf --- rutherfordium	Db --- dubnium	Sg --- seaborgium	Bh --- bohrium	Hs --- hassium	Mt --- meitnerium	Ds --- darmstadtium	Rg --- roentgenium	Uub --- ununbium	Uut --- ununtrium	Uuq --- ununquadium	Uup --- ununpentium	Uuh --- ununhexium		Uuo --- ununoctium

A Natural Approach to Chemistry

Isotope Periodic Table
(first four rows)

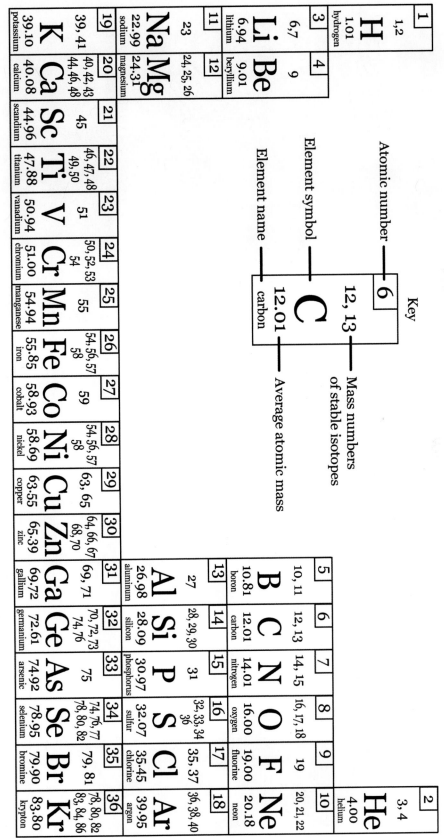

Laboratory Equipment

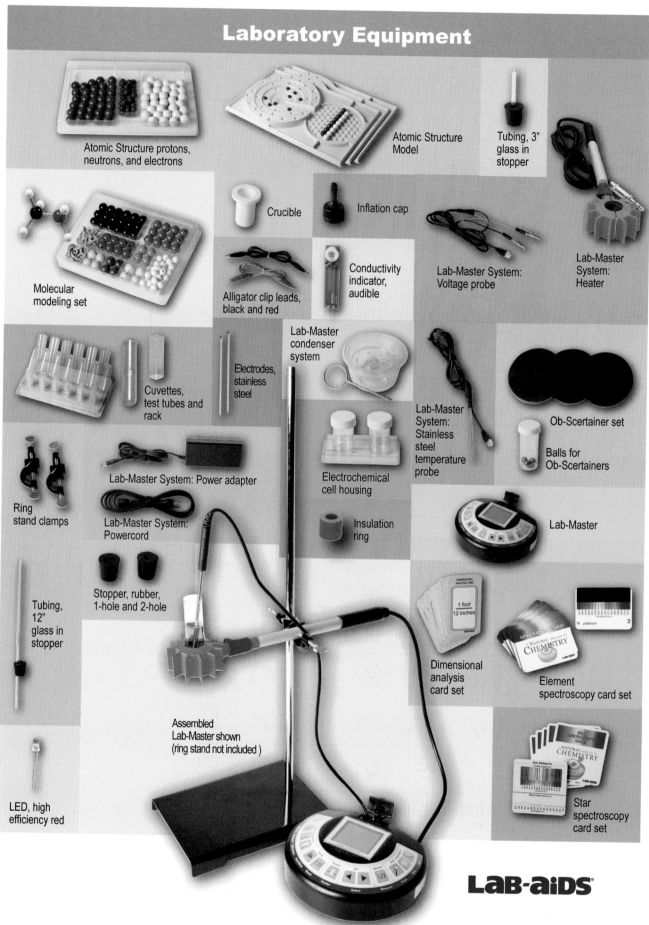

Atomic Structure protons, neutrons, and electrons

Atomic Structure Model

Tubing, 3" glass in stopper

Molecular modeling set

Crucible

Inflation cap

Alligator clip leads, black and red

Conductivity indicator, audible

Lab-Master System: Voltage probe

Lab-Master System: Heater

Cuvettes, test tubes and rack

Electrodes, stainless steel

Lab-Master condenser system

Lab-Master System: Stainless steel temperature probe

Ob-Scertainer set

Balls for Ob-Scertainers

Ring stand clamps

Lab-Master System: Power adapter

Lab-Master System: Powercord

Electrochemical cell housing

Insulation ring

Lab-Master

Tubing, 12" glass in stopper

Stopper, rubber, 1-hole and 2-hole

1 foot
12 inches

Dimensional analysis card set

Element spectroscopy card set

Assembled Lab-Master shown (ring stand not included)

Star spectroscopy card set

LED, high efficiency red

LaB-aiDS

Units and Constants

In chemistry we perform many measurements of physical properties such as temperature, mass etc.

Every measurement consists of two parts:

1. the *number* that tells us the quantity of what we are measuring and
2. the *unit* that tells us what was measured.

For example, when we measure temperature we can't just say it is 27 or even 27 degrees. We must also specify the unit. We should say 27°C or 27°F, whatever the unit might be that we are working with. There is a big difference between 27°C and 27°F.

Table 1. SI base units

Quantity	Unit	Symbol
length	meter	m
mass	kilogram	kg
time	second	s
electric current	ampere	A
thermodynamic temperature	kelvin	K
amount of substance	mole	mol
luminous intensity	candela	cd

Table 2. SI derived units

Derived quantity	Name	Symbol
area	square meter	m^2
volume	cubic meter	m^3
speed, velocity	meter per second	m/s
acceleration	meter per second squared	m/s^2
wave number	reciprocal meter	m^{-1}
mass density	kilogram per cubic meter	kg/m^3
specific volume	cubic meter per kilogram	m^3/kg
current density	ampere per square meter	A/m^2
magnetic field strength	ampere per meter	A/m
amount-of-substance concentration	mole per cubic meter	mol/m^3
luminance	candela per square meter	cd/m^2

Table 3. Fundamental constants and useful parameters of nature

Quantity	Symbol	Value	Units
Absolute zero	0 K	−273.15	°C
Strength of gravity at Earth's surface	g	9.8	N/kg or m/s^2
Avogadro's number	N_A	6.02×10^{23}	atoms/mole
Boltzmann's constant	k	1.381×10^{-23}	J/K
Electron mass	m_e	9.109×10^{-31}	kg
Proton mass	m_p	1.673×10^{-27}	kg
Neutron mass	m_n	1.675×10^{-27}	kg
Planck's constant	h	6.626×10^{-34}	J · s
Stefan–Boltzmann constant	s	5.670×10^{-8}	W/m^2/kg^2
Speed of light in vacuum	c	2.998×10^{8}	m/s
Universal gravitational constant	G	6.670×10^{-11}	N · m^2/kg^2
Elementary charge	e	1.602×10^{-19}	coulombs (C)
Speed of sound at 20°C	v_s	343	m/s
Gas constant for air	R	287.1	J/kg · K
Coulomb's law constant	K	9×10^{9}	N · m^2/C^2
Earth: mass	m_{earth}	5.98×10^{24}	kg
Earth: radius	r_{earth}	6.38×10^{6}	m
Moon: mass	m_{moon}	7.36×10^{22}	kg
Moon: radius	r_{moon}	1.74×10^{6}	m
Sun: mass	m_{sun}	1.99×10^{30}	kg
Sun: radius	r_{sun}	6.96×10^{8}	m

Table 4. Scientific notation

Numbers smaller than 1	Prefix, if applicable	Word for, if applicable	Numbers larger than 1	Prefix, if applicable	Word for, if applicable
10^{-12}= 0.000 000 000 001	pico-	trillionth	10^{1} = 10	deka-	ten
10^{-11}= 0.000 000 000 01			10^{2} = 100	hekato-	hundred
10^{-10}= 0.000 000 000 1			10^{3} = 1,000	kilo-	thousand
10^{-9} = 0.000 000 001	nano-	billionth	10^{4} = 10,000		
10^{-8} = 0.000 000 01			10^{5} = 100,000		
10^{-7} = 0.000 000 1			10^{6} = 1,000,000	mega-	million
10^{-6} = 0.000 001	micro-	millionth	10^{7} = 10,000,000		
10^{-5} = 0.000 01			10^{8} = 100,000,000		
10^{-4} = 0.000 1			10^{9} = 1,000,000,000	giga-	billion
10^{-3} = 0.001	milli-	thousandth	10^{10} = 10,000,000,000		
10^{-2} = 0.01	centi-	hundredth	10^{11} = 100,000,000,000		
10^{-1} = 0.1	deci-	tenth	10^{12} = 1,000,000,000,000	tera-	trillion

Time
1 hour = 60 minutes = 3,600 seconds
1 day = 1,440 minutes = 8.64×10^4 seconds
1 year = 365.25 days = 3.156×10^7 seconds

Angles and angular speed
1 radian = 57.3
1 degree = 0.01745 radians
1 rad/s = 9.549 rev/min (rpm)

Length
1 centimeter (cm) = 0.394 inches (in) = 0.0328 feet (ft)
1 meter (m) = 100 centimeters (cm) = 39.37 inches (in)
1 kilometer (km) = 1,000 meters = 0.6215 miles (mi)
1 miles (mi) = 5,280 feet (ft) = 1,609 kilometers (km)

Area
$1 \text{ m}^2 = 10,000 \text{ cm}^2 = 10.76 \text{ ft}^2 = 1,550 \text{ in}^2$
$1 \text{ in}^2 = 6.452 \text{ cm}^2 = 0.000645 \text{ m}^2$
$1 \text{ acre} = 43,560 \text{ ft}^2 = 4,048 \text{ m}^2$

Volume
$1 \text{ m}^3 = 1,000 \text{ liters} = 10^6 \text{ cm}^3 = 35.32 \text{ ft}^3 = 264.2 \text{ gallons}$
$1 \text{ gallon} = 3.785 \text{ liters} = 0.003785 \text{ m}^3$

Speed
1 m/s = 2.237 mi/hr = 3.600 km/hr
1 mi/hr = 0.4470 m/s = 1.609 km/hr

Mass
1 kilogram (kg) = 1,000 grams (g)
1 atomic mass unit (amu) = 1.660×10^{-27} kg

Force
1 newton (N) = 0.2248 pounds (lb)
1 pound (lb) = 4.448 newtons (N)

Pressure
1 pascal (Pa) = $1 \text{ N/m}^2 = 1.450 \times 10^{-4} \text{ lb/in}^2$ (psi)
1 lb/in^2 (psi) = $6,895 \text{ N/m}^2$ (Pa)
1 atmosphere (atm) = 14.70 lb/in^2 (psi) = $101,300 \text{ N/m}^2$ (Pa)

Energy
1 kilowatt · hour (kwh) = 3.6×10^6 joules (J)
1 British thermal unit (BTU) = 1,054 joules (J)
1 electron volt (eV) = 1.602×10^{-19} joules (J)
$1 \text{ J} = 1 \text{ N} \cdot \text{m} = 9.484 \times 10^{-4} \text{ BTU} = 2.778 \times 10^{-7}$ kwh

Power
1 watt (W) = 1 J/s = 0.001341 horsepower (hp)
1 horsepower (hp) = 745.7 watts (W)

Temperature
$$T_{Celsius} = \frac{5}{9}(T_{Fahrenheit} - 32) \qquad T_{Fahrenheit} = \frac{5}{9}T_{Celsius} + 32$$

$$T\text{ (K)} = T_{Celsius} + 273.15$$

Unit conversion examples: dimensional analysis.

1.   Convert 12.5 gallons to liters.

$$12.5 \text{ gallons} \times \frac{3.785 \text{ L}}{\text{gallon}} = 12.5 \times 3.785 \text{ L} = 41.3 \text{ L}$$

2.   Convert 750 ppm (parts per million) of NaCl solution to molarity (M)

1 ppm means that we have one part in one million, or 1 ppm = 1/1,000,000.

Then 200 ppm of NaCl means that we have

$$\frac{200 \text{ g NaCl}}{1,000,000 \text{ g solution}} = \frac{2 \text{ g NaCl}}{10,000 \text{ g of solution}}$$

So this is the same as

$$\frac{0.2 \text{ g NaCl}}{1,000 \text{ mL of solution}} = \frac{0.2 \text{ g NaCl}}{1 \text{ L of solution}}$$

Now need to find how many moles are in 0.2 g of NaCl. The molecular weight of NaCl is 23.0 + 35.0 = 58.5 g/mole,

so 0.2 g of NaCl is $\dfrac{0.2 \text{ g}}{58.5 \text{ g/mole}} = 0.00342$ moles

So 200 ppm NaCl is $\dfrac{0.00342 \text{ moles}}{1 \text{ L of solution}} = 0.00342$ M

Chemistry Mathematics - Significant Figures

A small number of mathematical skills are required in order to study chemistry. Grasping these basic skills will help us gain a deeper understanding of the science of chemistry. Here we will review the most useful of these skills.

Algebraic equations

An algebraic equation is a mathematical expression that relates various parameters. For example, the equation that relates density (D), volume (V) and mass (m) is

$$D = m / V$$

This equation may also be written in the following two ways:

$$V = m / D$$

$$m = D \times V$$

With these equations we can calculate any of the three parameters (D, V, or m) if we know the other two.

Another important equation in chemistry is the ideal gas law which is

$$P V = n R T$$

In this equation P is the pressure, V is the volume, T is the temperature, R is the gas constant, and n is the number of moles of a gas.

If we for example have an experiment where we measure the temperature and the volume of a gas and want to know the pressure we manipulate the equation as follows: Eliminate V by dividing both sides by V.

$$\frac{P \cancel{V}}{\cancel{V}} = \frac{n R T}{V}$$

By canceling V as shown above we have

$$P = \frac{n R T}{V}$$

Scientific notation

When we encounter very small or very large numbers we use scientific notation to express them. The general form of a number written in scientific notation is

$$A \times 10^n$$

A is a number between 1 and 10 and the exponent n is a number that can be positive or negative and represents the power of 10. Let's practice by converting a few numbers to scientific notation.

1. Convert 254 to scientific notation.
   Here $A = 2.54$ and $n = 2$. This means that the number 2.54 is multiplied by two factors of 10 or 100: $2.54 \times 100 = 254$.

   The number 100 we write as 10^2 and the number in scientific notation is 2.54×10^2.

2. Convert –3,456 to scientific notation.
   In this case $A = -3.456$ and $n = 3$. Note that the negative sign is carried along.
   The number in scientific notation is -3.456×10^3.

3. Convert 0.0125 to scientific notation.
   This number is less than one. Here $A = 1.25$ and n has to be chosen so that when 10^n is multiplied by 1.25 we obtain 0.0125. To go from 1.25 to 0.0125 we have to move the decimal point to the left by two positions. Each movement of the decimal point to the left corresponds to a division by 10. In this case since we moved two positions to the left $n = -2$.
   The number in scientific notation is 1.25×10^{-2}.

4. Here is another example. Convert 0.000567 to scientific notation.
   Here $A = 5.67$. Do you agree that $n = -4$?
   So, the number in scientific notation is 5.67×10^{-4}.

Now let's practice going the other way: From scientific notation to the usual form.

1. Convert 5.23×10^4 to usual form.
   Here we have $A = 5.23$ and $n = 4$.
   So we have to move the decimal point four places to the right.
   $5.23 \times 10^4 = 52,300$

2. Convert 6.67×10^{-3} to usual form.
   Here we have $A = 6.67$ and $n = -3$.
   So we have to move the decimal point four places to the left (since n is negative).
   Then $6.67 \times 10^{-3} = 0.00667$.

Here are some conversions for you to work out:

Convert the following numbers to scientific notation.

   a. –0.0034
   b. 45,670
   c. 12.67

Convert the following from scientific notation to the usual form.

   a. -3.567×10^{-3}
   b. -2.34×10^6
   c. 6.67×10^{-3}

168

Logarithms

The logarithm of a number x is denoted by log x. The logarithm is used in calculating the pH of a solution and so it a very important thing to know.

Let's understand how logarithms work by finding the logarithm of the number 100.

If we call this unknown number y then $y = \log 100$.

y is the number that we have to raise the power of 10 so that $10^y = 100$. So y must be equal to 2 and $\log 100 = 2$.

The logarithm we just described has a base of 10 and it is sometimes written as $\log_{10} x$.

The base of the logarithm can be any number. In science we encounter the logarithm with base 10 and the so-called natural logarithm for which the base is the number 2.71828. This number is very useful in science and engineering and is denoted by the symbol $e = 2.71828$, which is also found in most scientific calculators.

So the natural logarithm of a number x is denoted by $\log_e x$ or as ln x, where the symbol ln is used for $\log_e$.

Regardless of the base all logarithms obey the same fundamental properties:

1. $\log_a 1 = 0$
2. $\log_a (A/B) = \log_a A - \log_a B$
3. $\log_a (A+B) = \log_a A + \log_a B$
4. $\log_a A^m = m \log_a A$

Let's review the concept of pH. (For a detailed description go to Chapter 13 of your textbook).

If the concentration of H^+ in a solution is 6.00×10^{-5} M, what is the pH of the solution?

Using our calculator we find that $\log(6.00 \times 10^{-5}) = -4.2218$ and so the pH is 4.2 which indicates an acidic solution.

> **Definition of pH**
>
> $$pH = -\log[H^+]$$
>
> pH is –1 times the logarithm of the H^+ molarity

Solved problem

A solution of acetic acid (CH_3COOH) has an H^+ concentration of 1×10^{-5} M. What is the pH of the solution?

Asked: *What is the pH?*

Given: *Molarity of H^+ is 1.00×10^{-5}*

Relationships: *pH $= -1 \times \log(H^+$ molarity$)$*

Solve: *need to find the number y which, when we raise 10 to its power $10^y = 1.00 \times 10^{-5}$*

So, pH $= -\log(1.00 \times 10^{-5}) = 5.0$

Answer: *The pH of the solution is 5.0*

Graphing

The best way to represent scientific data is with a graph. A graph is a visual representation of data and it gives us the opportunity to see the trend of the data and understand and describe physical phenomena.

The following must be considered when we want to create a graph from a set of data.

1.   The range of the data values. What is the smallest and the largest number in the data?

2.   The spread of the data. What is the largest and the smallest difference between data points?

Let's look at the set of data in Table 1 and see how we can plot them.

This is an interesting set of data since the range is very large and the spread between points is also very large. The following three graphs plot the data with different axes.

Table 1. Pesticide data

Pesticide Concentration (ppm)	Signal
1,000,000	5,210
100,000	495
10,000	52
1,000	5
100	0.45
10	0.05
1	0.0054
0.1	0.0006
0.01	0.000046
0.001	0.000005
0.0001	0.0000005

Data plotted on a linear–linear scale

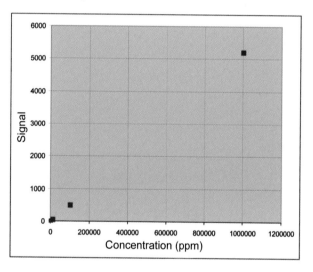

Which plot do you think gives the best visual representation of the data?

Data plotted on a linear–log scale

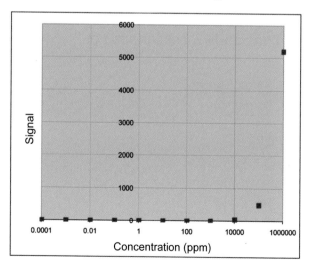

Data plotted on log–log scale

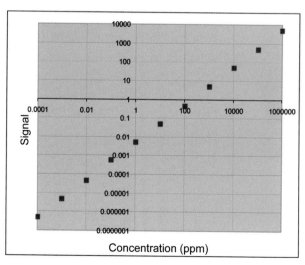

Significant figures

The numbers that we get when we measure or calculate something have a certain amount of uncertainty associated with them. For example, when we use a tape measure to see how tall we are we are able to do it to within a certain accuracy. For example 179 cm. Someone might perform the same measurement with a different tape measure that is more accurate - has more divisions - and find that the height is 178.6 cm.

The measurement of 179 cm has 3 significant figures and the measurement of 178.6 has four significant figures.

Significant figures are all the digits in a measured or calculated value that are known with certainty plus one digit that is uncertain.

The rules for writing and using significant figures when we perform measurements or calculations are as follows:

1.   In numbers that do not contain zeros, all digits are significant.
     23 has two significant figures.
     –13.45 has four significant figures.
     12,345 has five significant figures.

2.   When zeros are contained in a number we count significant figures as follows:
     a.   If the zero is between other digits they count as significant.
          203 has three significant figures.
          20.25 has four significant figures.
     b.   A leading zero is not significant.
          0.05 has one significant figure.
          –0.00125 has three significant figures.
     c.   A zero at the end is significant when it is to the right of the decimal point.
          10.20 has four significant figures.
          23.020 has five significant figures.

Rounding off

Electronic calculators display a large number of digits. Many of these digits are not relevant and so we should learn how to round off the number correctly. Before we round off numbers we must first decide how many significant figures we need, then we apply the following rules for rounding.

1.   If the first digit to the right of the significant figure is less than 5, then that digit and all other digits that follow it are dropped.
     a.   The number 2.234563 rounded to three digits becomes 2.23.
     b.   The number 0.024356 rounded to two significant figures becomes 0.024.

2.   If the first digit to the right of the significant figure is greater than 5, the significant digit is increased by one.
     a.   The number 23.36 rounded to three digits becomes 23.4.
     b.   The number 0.004356 rounded to two significant figures becomes 0.0044.

Addition and Subtraction

When we add or subtract numerical quantities, the answer should have the same number of decimal places as the quantity with the smallest number of decimal places.

Here are some examples:

1. We have an experiment where we add the following solutions to a test tube: 12.0, 13.5, and 15.60 mL. When we plug these numbers in the calculator we get 41.1 mL.
    The answer is 41.1.

2. Now let's add 12, 13.5, and 15.60 mL.
    When we plug these numbers in the calculator we get 41.17 mL.
    The answer is 41

3. Now let's add 12.05, 13.558, and 15.60 mL.
    When we plug these numbers in the calculator we get 41.208 mL.
    The answer is 41.21

4. Now let's add 12.05, 980.45, and 15.60 mL.
    When we plug these numbers in the calculator we get 1,008.1 mL.
    The answer is 1,008.10. This time the calculator gave us too few significant figures.

Multiplication and division

When we multiply or divide, the number of significant figures in the answer should be the same as in the number with the smallest number of significant figures.

Here are some examples:

1. Suppose that you measure the volume of a solution to be 23.0 mL and the mass of the solution to be 15.3 g. You calculate the density (15.3 g/23.0 mL) with your calculator and get 0.66521739. What is the correct number to report for the density?
    The answer is 0.665 g/mL

2. Now let's multiply 0.0234 by 12.35.
    When we plug these numbers in the calculator we get 0.28899.
    The answer is 0.289.

3. Now let's divide 2 by 3.
    When we plug these numbers in the calculator we get 0.666666.
    The answer is 0.7.

4. Now let's divide 2.0 by 3.0.
    When we plug these numbers in the calculator we again get 0.666666.
    The answer is 0.67.

Lab-Master User Manual

The Lab-Master is a device specifically designed to perform all experiments in an introductory chemistry class. This user manual presents the basic operating features of the device and shows the user how to perform the fundamental measurements and controls used in chemistry.

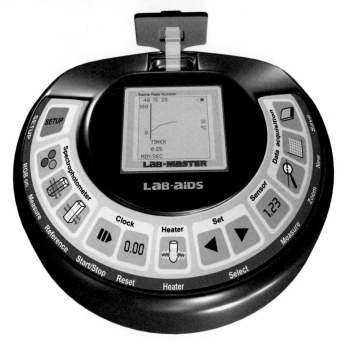

The main features of the device are the following:

- temperature and voltage measurement capability with automatic sensor recognition
- test tube heater with accurate temperature control
- spectrophotometer with calibration features
- rechargeable battery
- graphic screen
- data storage ability
- SD card data transfer

Setting up

- **Turning on the device:**

  The on/off switch is on the bottom right side of the device.

- **Connecting the power**

  Lab-Master accepts 18 V line DC and it is connected on the back side as shown on the picture. The battery of the device is rechargeable and should not be removed or replaced by the user.

- **Sensor connections**

  All sensors are connected at the sensor port. Sensors are recognized automatically by the device.

- **Heater connection**

  The heater device is connected at the dedicated port. The device automatically recognizes that the heater is connected.

- **SD card/data access port**

  The data stored in the device can be downloaded using a standard SD card.

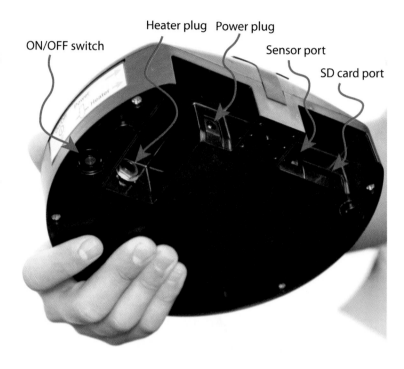

The card is inserted at the SD port and it is recognized automatically by the device.

The keypad

The buttons on the keypad are arranged by function. The main groups are:

- **Spectrophotometer:**

  Controls all functions for the RGB spectrophotometer

- **Heater:**

  Engages the heater menu.

- **SETUP:**

  Sets device name and data mode and rate.

- **Clock:**

  Starts, Stops and Resets the clock.

- **Sensor:**

  Used when data are acquired manually.

- **Data Acquisition:**

  Saves data to memory and starts new experiments.

- **Set:**

  Used to navigate through the various modes.

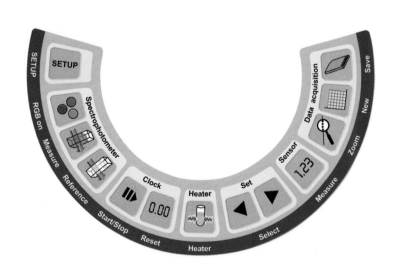

174

Starting and stopping the timer

The timer of the Lab-master may be used as a stopwatch and as a way to control when to start and when to stop an experiment.
To start and stop the timer use the **Start/Stop** key.

To reset the timer use the **Reset** key.

How to measure temperature

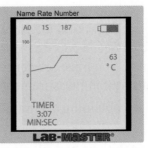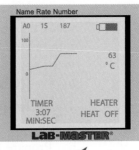

1. Turn on the Lab-Master.
2. Connect the temperature probe to the device.
3. The temperature sensor is recognized automatically and the device starts taking data every second continuously.
4. If the 18 V line power and the heater are connected, the display will indicate this as shown on the this screen image.
5. If you wish to save the data at any time just press the **Save** button.
6. To download the data just insert the SD card and the data are automatically downloaded.

How to measure voltage

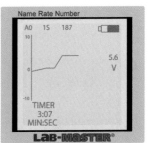

1. Turn on the Lab-Master.
2. Connect the voltage probe to the device.
3. The voltage sensor is recognized automatically and the device starts taking data every second continuously.
4. Every other function is similar to the temperature.

Taking data at a specified rate

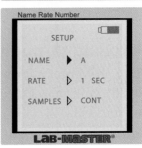

If you wish to take data at a rate other than the default value (1 per second and continuously) use the **SETUP** mode as follows:

1. Press the **SETUP** button.
2. Now you have the option to change the NAME, the RATE, and the number of SAMPLES.
3. Press the left or right arrows to navigate within each option.
4. Press the **SETUP** button to move through the options.
5. For the RATE you have the following choices:
   1 SEC, 5 SEC, 10 SEC, 30 SEC, 1 MIN, 5 MIN, 10 MIN, 30 MIN, 1 HOUR, USER. By selecting, for example, 30 SEC, the device will take a data point every 30 s.
   By selecting USER, the device will take data only when you press the measure button.
6. For the SAMPLES you have the following choices:
   CONT, 5, 10, 25, 50, 100, 200.
7. For example, if you would like to take a data point every 1 minute for 10 minutes you select:
   RATE = 1 MIN and SAMPLES = 10.

How to measure absorption

1. Press the **RGB on** button.
2. Now you must calibrate the device by pressing the **Reference** button.
3. Insert the cuvette you are using for reference in the spectrophotometer cell holder and press the **Reference** button. Your device is now ready to measure the absorption of your samples. If you try to take an absorption measurement without first referencing the device, a NO REFERENCE indicator appears to warn you about it. You must reference the device in order to be able to take RGB absorption measurements.

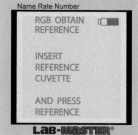

4. The technique for obtaining accurate RGB measurements is as follows:

    a. Prepare the solutions and fill all cuvettes to the same level including the reference cuvette.
    b. Insert the reference cuvette and reference the device.

    c. With the reference cuvette still in the cell holder press the **Measure** button. All readings should be close to zero.
    d. Insert the cuvettes with the samples and take the RGB absorbance measurements.

Scrolling through data

The Lab-Master allows you to, while taking data, go back and review the data already collected. Let's assume that we have taken a number of RGB data points and now want to see the previous data.

The procedure is as follows:

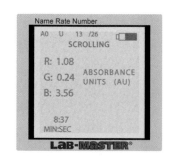

1. Press the left or right arrow button.
2. The word SCROLLING appears with the numbers 13 / 26 above it. The number 13 means that the device now displays the 13th point out of a total of 26 points. The data values correspond to the data of the 13th point.
3. You may navigate through the entire data set by using the left or right arrows.
4. To exit from the scrolling mode, navigate to the end of the data set. Note that by holding the left or right key down you can fast forward through the data.

How to use the heater

1. To use the heater the line power must be connected to the Lab-Master. The device automatically detects if the power whether connected and will not allow access to the heater interface if it is not connected.

2. Press the **Heater** button to enter the heater screen menu.

3. If the heater is not connected the device displays the HEATER IS NOT CONNECTED enunciator. Connect the heater to proceed. The device automatically detects when the heater is connected.

4. In the heater screen menu you can select the SETPOINT temperature and the CONTROL method.

5. The SETPOINT temperature can be selected by pressing the right and left arrows. You may select any temperature between 1°C and 150°C. You may increment the values by 1°C or hold down the arrow key for scrolling by 10°C increments.

6. When the temperature probe is not connected the CONTROL option is limited to HTR. When the temperature probe is connected, the CONTROL options are HTR and PROBE which will be discussed in the next section.

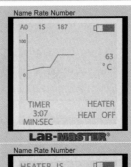

How to heat a solution to a specified temperature

As an example let's assume that we want to heat a solution in the test tube to a temperature of 47°C. We will go through the procedure of how to do that. The procedure is then the same for any other solution temperature.

1. Turn on the Lab-Master and connect power, heater, and temperature probe.

2. Press the **Heater** button.

3. Scroll through the SETPOINT and select the temperature of 41°C.

4. Press **Heater** again to activate the CONTROL option.

5. Press the right arrow to select PROBE. (Note that the PROBE selection is not available if the temperature probe is not connected.)

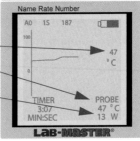

6. Press **Heater** to exit

7. Press the **Start/Stop** button to start the experiment.

8. The display shows the following information:

   a. the actual solution temperature

   b. the desired solution temperature

   c. the instantaneous power that is applied to the heater

9. While running this experiment, remember to stir the solution gently and continuously and make sure you do not remove the temperature probe from the solution.

How to store data to memory

1. At any time while you are performing measurements you may press the **Save** button to record the data into the memory of the Lab-Master.

2. While the data are being saved the SAVING . . enunciator is shown.

3. When saving is complete press **Start/Stop** to resume taking measurements.

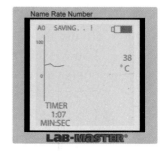

How to transfer data

1. Insert the SD card in the device. The data are downloaded automatically.

2. Once the data transfer is complete the screen indicates 100% completion and you may now remove the card.

How to extract data from the SD card

1. Insert the SD card into your computer and open it. The directories look like the screen shot on the right.

2. Locate the directory with your device name and open it with your spreadsheet program.

3. The data appear in column form, which may be plotted by any software or spreadsheet program as shown in this example.

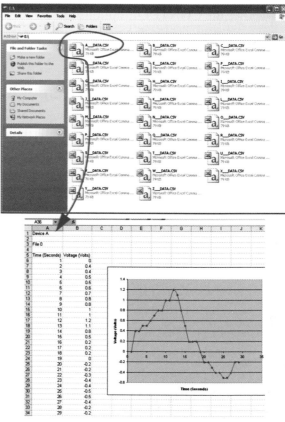

How to reprogram the device

When Lab-Master software is upgraded you may download the software and upgrade your device with the latest software free of charge.

The procedure is as follows:

1. Download the file containing the latest software from the Lab-Aids Web page.

2. Insert the SD card in your computer.

3. Copy the new software file onto your SD card

4. Insert the SD card into the Lab-Master.

5. The Lab-Master automatically recognizes the presence of the new software REFLASH file on the SD card and asks you to confirm the reprograming or skip it.

6. Once you confirm, the reprograming takes only a few seconds and your new software is ready to use.

Your College Experience: Strategies for Success, 12/e: ALL YOU NEED FOR COLLEGE SUCCESS

John N. Gardner · Betsy O. Barefoot
Student edition: ISBN 978-1-4576-9966-5
Loose-leaf version: ISBN 978-1-319-01251-9 (priced about 65% of the traditional text)
e-Books available (priced at approximately 50% of the traditional text)

Written by the leading authorities on the first-year seminar and grounded in research, *Your College Experience* by **John N. Gardner** and **Betsy O. Barefoot** offers today's diverse students the practical help they need to make the transition to college and get the most out of their time there. While maintaining its hallmark theme of goal setting, the Twelfth Edition reflects a focus on practical strategies across all topics of the book to help students be successful from the start. Chapters on Emotional Intelligence, Thinking in College, and Wellness have all been reorganized and thoroughly revised to be more relevant and useful for today's students.

A full package of instructional support materials—including an Instructor's Annotated Edition, Instructor's Manual and Test Bank, PowerPoint slides, videos, and powerful new digital resources—provides new and experienced instructors with the tools they need to engage students in this course and increase retention.

HELPING STUDENTS SUCCEED FROM THE START

Chapter 1 introduces students to the concepts of purpose and goal setting and explores the value of higher education. New content in the chapter includes a summary of high-impact practices, a discussion of the role of peer leaders in the college success course, material on academic planning and working with an academic adviser, and an emphasis on the concept of resilience.

Assess Your Strengths & Set Goals boxes in each chapter ask students to identify their strengths and then set goals around their own objectives for the chapter material.

Getting the Most Out of College: High-Impact Practices

high-impact practices 1–10

Throughout your college experience, you will have the opportunity to participate in activities known as "high-impact practices." High-impact practices are particular activities that research shows have significant positive impact on both your learning and your overall success. One high-impact practice is taking the first-year seminar, which shouldn't surprise you given what you have read in this chapter about the value of this course. Here is a comprehensive list of the ten high-impact practices in which you can participate, listed in the order you are most likely to encounter them. (In this textbook, this icon ⟲ is used to alert you to these opportunities to enrich your learning.):

1. **first-year seminars** The course in which you find yourself now, designed to prepare you for your college experience.
2. **writing-intensive courses** Courses across the curriculum that engage you in multiple forms of writing for different audiences. This textbook offers various writing activities that make your first-year seminar a writing-intensive course.
3. **collaborative assignments** Learning activities in which you work and solve problems with your classmates in this and other courses.
4. **global learning or diversity experiences** Courses and programs in which you explore cultures, life experiences, and worldviews different from your own.
5. **service-learning** Programs or courses in which you engage in required field-based "experiential learning" and reflection while giving back to your community through service.
6. **learning communities** Programs in which you would take two or more "linked" courses with a group of other students and work closely with one another and with your instructors.
7. **campus-wide common intellectual experiences** Programs in which you would take required "common-core" courses, participate in a required learning community, or engage in other shared experiences such as a "common reading."
8. **undergraduate research** A program that gives you the opportunity to participate in systematic investigation and research working one-

assess **your** strengths

Think about the topic of this chapter. Do you already have a good understanding of the benefits of college? Do you have a clear sense of purpose? What personal and career goals do you want to pursue in college? Describe the experience you have with setting goals and reaching them. If you are not quite ready to answer these questions yet, return to them as you read through this chapter.

set goals

Think about a challenge you have had in the past with understanding what college is all about or setting personal goals. As you read this chapter, set a goal that relates to chapter material, and be prepared to talk with others in your class about why you selected this goal. For example, you might set a goal to understand the research on the value of a college degree and apply it to your own perso

New coverage of academic planning and working with an academic adviser highlights for students the value of using these resources from the start.

Working with an Academic Adviser

Before you register for classes next term, sit down for a strategy session with your academic adviser. On most campuses, you'll be assigned an adviser, who is usually an instructor or a staff person in your chosen field of study. Some colleges offer special advisory centers run by professional advisers. A good adviser can help you choose courses, decide on a major, weigh career possibilities, and map out your degree and certificate requirements. Your adviser can also recommend instructors and help you simplify all aspects of your academic life, so it's important to meet with your adviser right away. Here are a few ways to make sure that your first meeting is a valuable experience.

- **Prepare for the meeting by looking at the course catalog, thinking about available majors, and familiarizing yourself with campus**

ACADEMIC PLANNING

If you have a goal to drive across the United States, you could, in theory, hop in a car that may need an oil change and travel without GPS or an itinerary and without a carefully packed bag or a planned

MOTIVATING STUDENTS TO BE RESILIENT, CONNECT, AND THINK CRITICALLY

Features, all presented through a dynamic new design, help students engage in the course.

Is This You? boxes speak directly to students who are likely taking first-year experience courses. Look for these special messages to first-generation college students, returning students, student athletes, and students encountering common first-year issues such as time-management challenges, difficulty with writing assignments, weight gain, financial problems, and the clash of new ideas with old beliefs.

is**this**you?

Bouncing Back from a Bad Grade

You bombed a test, and now you are feeling hopeless and unsure about how to do better. First, know that a bad grade is not the end of the world. Almost every student performs poorly at some point in college. Don't let one D or F get you down. Use the opportunity to build your resilience—to become stronger and show your tough spirit. One way to bounce back from disappointment is to take control of the situation. Talk to the course instructor, work to understand what went wrong, and develop a strategy for improvement. That strategy might be finding a tutor, meeting on a regular basis with your instructor, or working with a learning center professional who can help you improve your skills in reading, studying, remembering, and preparing for tests. Your college success instructor can help you decide what first steps you need to take to improve your academic performance.

is**this**you?

Older than Average

Are you an older student, maybe in your thirties or forties, who is back in college? As an adult, you probably have a great deal of life experience in dealing with tough times. You might have real strengths in emotional intelligence that you have developed at work, at home, or with your family, but you may also have some areas that you need to improve. How are you using your skills to stand up for yourself and negotiate with others as you face the challenges of college? Using your existing strengths and skills in college could allow you to be a role model for others. You might want to give some advice to younger students who seem to be struggling with the day-to-day interactions that are part of college life and help those students find ways to be more adaptable, resilient, and assertive.

Your Turn collaborative learning activities foster peer-to-peer communication, collaboration, motivation, good decision making, writing and reflection, and critical thinking. These activities can be used in class, as homework, or as group activities to strengthen the bond between students and their college communities. They are organized into four types based on what students are asked to do: Make Good Choices, Stay Motivated, Work Together, and Write and Reflect.

your**turn** Stay Motivated

Academic Planning

You have probably already met with an academic adviser, but if not, schedule a meeting right away. Think about this meeting and what you accomplished. Then write a short paper or journal entry about something you learned that increased your motivation to take academic planning seriously. Also, describe in writing at least three problems you might encounter when it comes to choosing your major or planning your program of study if you do not take academic planning seriously. How can these possible negative consequences increase your motivation to plan well for your next meeting with your adviser?

your**turn** Make Good Choices

Facebook through an Employer's Eyes

Look at your own or a friend's Facebook page. Do you see anything that puts you or your friend in a negative light? Think about how you would alter the content and writing style if this Facebook page were part of a job application. Consider the changes that are needed to give you or your friend a good chance of getting the job. Remember that employers now routinely check Facebook to see what kinds of information potential employees might post. Choose to post only information that you are willing to share with anyone—*especially* a potential employer.

your**turn** Write and Reflect

Are You Able to Concentrate?

The next time that you read a textbook, monitor your ability to concentrate. Check your watch when you begin, and check it again when your mind begins to wander. How many minutes did you concentrate on your reading? List some strategies to keep your mind from wandering. Write a journal entry containing ideas you have heard that you think will work well for you.

HOW EMOTIONS INFLUENCE SUCCESS

Accentuate the Positive
You probably know people who always find the negative in any situation. Constantly focusing on what's missing or what's not perfect will likely make you the kind of person whom others avoid. Practice looking on the bright side.
marekuliasz/Shutterstock

Emotions are strongly tied to physical and psychological well-being. For example, some studies have suggested that cancer patients who have strong EI live longer than those with weak EI. People who are aware of the needs of others tend to be happier than people who are not.

An extensive study done at the University of Pennsylvania found that the best athletes succeed in part because they're extremely optimistic. A number of studies link strong EI skills to college success in particular. Studies indicate that emotionally intelligent students get higher grades. Researchers looked at students' grade point averages at the end of their first year of college. Students who had tested high for intrapersonal skills, stress tolerance, and adaptability when they entered in the fall did better academically than those who had lower overall EI test scores. Here are a few other highlights of those studies:

- **Motivation:** Motivation is one of the most important attributes that college students can have. Figuring out what actually does motivate anyone is complex, but striving to find out and nurture these motivations is the goal.
- **Resilience:** We discussed resilience above—stronger emotional intelligence leads to greater resilience. Students with healthy emotional intelligence might act proactively by asking instructors for feedback on projects, papers, and tests, participating in classroom discussions, and joining study groups. Students with unhealthy EI are likely to struggle academically, panic before taking tests, have trouble concentrating on coursework, and engage in risky behaviors such as alcohol and drug abuse in an effort to cope. Dr. Richard Kadison, a former director of mental health services at Harvard University, noted that "the emotional well-being of students goes hand in hand with their academic development. If they're not doing well emotionally, they are not going to reach their academic potential."[2]

UNDERSTANDING WELLNESS

Wellness is a concept that encompasses the care of your mind, body, and spirit. Wellness involves making healthy choices and achieving balance throughout your life. It includes reducing stress in positive ways, keeping fit, fostering your spirituality, deepening your self-knowledge, maintaining good sexual health, and taking a safe approach to alcohol and other drugs—assuming that you are of legal age to consume them.

Take this short quiz. As you consider each question, rate yourself on a scale of 1–5, with 1 being "never" and 5 being "always."

1. Are you able to manage your stress successfully? _____
2. Do you eat a wide range of healthy foods? _____
3. Do you exercise at least once a day? _____
4. Do you get seven or more hours of sleep each night? _____
5. Do you say "no" to others in order to manage your obligations? _____
6. Do you seek help from friends, family, or professionals when you need it? _____
7. Are you in control of your sexual health? _____
8. Do you avoid abusing alcohol, tobacco, or other substances? _____
9. Do you live a balanced life? _____

In what areas did you mark a 4 or 5? _____
In what areas did you mark a 1 or 2? _____

As you read the preview of the nine components of wellness described on the next page, pay special attention to the areas that you scored as ones or twos, so that you can get yourself on track.

Tech Tips in each chapter introduce essential skills related to the moving target that is technology—proper use of e-mail, benefits of e-books, the value of specific programs and apps for good note taking, critically thinking when doing online research, building an appropriate and safe online persona, use of the cloud, and ways for students to use technology to join the professional communities that span life in college and beyond.

▶ ▶ ▶ ▶

PROVIDING IMPORTANT NEW CONTENT AND UPDATES WITH A FOCUS ON THREE CHAPTERS

The 12/e features revisions from cover to cover, with a focus on the following:

Chapter 3, Emotional Intelligence (EI), has been improved by linking EI concepts to events of daily college life, with elaboration on the concepts of resilience and making good choices. Self-assessments help students evaluate and improve their own EI.

Chapter 5, Thinking in College, gives students a better understanding of what is involved in college-level thinking, with practical strategies on how to achieve it. Students are clearly shown how concepts like fast and slow thinking, problem solving, creativity, and collaboration all relate to college-level thinking. The chapter includes a new critical-thinking assessment, a new application of Bloom's Taxonomy, and a heavily revised Tech Tip shown below.

Chapter 13, Wellness, takes a new, holistic view of wellness, with a major focus on stress and how to prevent it through proper nutrition, sleep, and exercise. The chapter includes a stress self-assessment exercise.

tech tip

USE YOUR CRITICAL-THINKING SKILLS IN CONDUCTING RESEARCH

You have probably heard that colleges and universities expect their students to be able to conduct research when they write papers or create projects. In high school or a casual setting, doing research usually means going to a search engine like Google, Yahoo, or Ask.com. Many of us do this so automatically that we say, "Let me 'Google' that." But is a Google search all professors are looking for when they ask you to conduct research? How else could you conduct research?

Internet searches will help you find people basically doing three things: **yelling**, **selling**, or **telling**.

Yelling: Someone has a viewpoint and puts it forward on Blogger or YouTube, but how do you know if they are biased or a member of a fringe or hate group when you use their video in your project?

Selling: Often, people promote products or services in a way that makes them sound like credible sources of information when they are really simply trying to get you to buy something.

Telling: These places and people actually have credible information that you find informative and useful, but how can you verify their credibility?

The Problem

You need to conduct research for a paper, but you're not sure how to evaluate the types of information found on the Internet.

The Fix *Use a critical-thinking system to conduct your research.*

Rommel Canlas/Shutterstock

How to Do It

Start with good questions. If you are researching a topic, such as "marijuana legalization," generate some questions you have about that subject rather than just going to Google and typing "marijuana" into the search box:

- What is the history of marijuana use in the U.S.
- Why was it made illegal in the first place?
- Where has it been legalized and why?
- What have been some of the positive and negative outcomes of making it legal?

Generating questions will save you time by clarifying what you need to know, so you will recognize useful results and ignore the ones that won't help you.

Go to the library. Show the reference librarians your list of questions. They can help you fine-tune them and will recommend good places to find certain kinds of answers.

Use databases. Your school pays for research databases, which collect a variety of credible, scholarly research. When you use research databases, you can be sure that the information is reliable, and you can refine your search terms to produce 20 or 30 returns, as opposed to 20 or 30 million. Most databases are available online with login information that your college can provide, so you can use them anytime from home or on your laptop.

Use a variety of locations to confirm information. When you see the same information in a variety of credible sources, you can start to trust its accuracy. *Remember that there are still good sources of information in print form that are not available online.*

Consider the quality of the information. Where did it come from? Who said it and why? How current is it? Has anything major happened in this area since this information was published?

EXTRA STYLE POINTS: Get in the habit of reading (not just watching) a variety of news and information sources. If you get news only from TV or links posted on Facebook, you will miss some important stories. Remember this: Professionals need to be up to date in their own areas of interest and expertise, but they also must be able to understand larger current events happening in the world around them. You must have broad knowledge in order to place your professional knowledge in context.

A COMPLETE PACKAGE OF INSTRUCTOR SUPPORT MATERIALS FOR NEW AND EXPERIENCED INSTRUCTORS.

The Instructor's Annotated Edition includes many new, clearly marked Retention Strategies in every chapter—best practices from John Gardner and Betsy Barefoot for keeping students in school. New Peer Leader annotations offer suggestions that peer ▶ ▶ ▶ leaders (or the instructor of record) can use in designing special activities. New High-Impact Practice (HIP) annotations give tips for incorporating HIP activities. In Class, Outside Class, and FYI annotations are also included.

Research conducted by colleges and universities has found that first-year students are far more likely to be successful if they participate in courses and programs designed to teach them how to succeed in college. This course is designed to help you avoid some of the pitfalls—both academic and personal—that trip up many beginning students.

Although your classmates might not say it out loud, many of them share your concerns, doubts, and fears about being in college. This course will provide a supportive environment in which you can share your successes and your frustrations, get to know others who are beginning college, develop lasting relationships with your instructor and some other students, and begin to think about your plans for life after college.

The Value of Your College Success Textbook

As college professors, researchers, and administrators with many years of experience working with first-year students, we're well aware that starting college can be challenging. We also know that if you apply the ideas in this book to your everyday life, you are likely to enjoy your time in college, graduate, and achieve your life goals.

Your instructor may ask you to read every chapter in this book, but even if you're not required to do so, consider this book a resource to answer questions you might have later this year and throughout your college experience. After this opening chapter, which discusses the value of college, purpose and goal setting, and academic planning, subsequent

RETENTION STRATEGY ❯ Make a positive prediction of your students' success as a result of taking this course by briefly explaining to them the pervasive research indicating that students who participate in college success courses are more likely to persist in and graduate from college than those who do not participate.

PEER LEADERS ❯ As a peer leader, you should take some time to relay your own experiences when you were a new college student—your hopes, doubts, and fears. If you took a college success course, be prepared to tell the students how you feel about it now. Looking back, was it fun? Was it helpful to you?

HIGH-IMPACT PRACTICE ❯ If the college success course on your campus is required of all or almost all first-year students, it also qualifies as a "campus-wide common intellectual experience," another high-impart practice.

ADDITIONAL SUPPORT MATERIALS

The Instructor's Manual and Test Bank includes everything you need to manage your course. New to this edition are sample syllabi for 16-, 12-, and 8-week courses; guidelines for incorporating e-Portfolios into a college success course; and capstone projects for the end of the course. The Test Bank is also available in a computerized version.

PowerPoint Slides include complete lecture outlines for each chapter of the book, plus images and figures from the text. Use as is or add your own material to make each presentation your own.

New! LaunchPad for *Your College Experience,* **12/e.** LaunchPad combines an interactive e-book with high-quality multimedia content and ready-made assessment options, including LearningCurve adaptive quizzing. Prebuilt units are easy to assign

or adapt to your material, such as readings, videos, quizzes, discussion groups, and more. LaunchPad also provides access to a grade book that provides a clear window on performance for your whole class, for individual students, and for individual assignments. The result is superior, book-specific content in a breakthrough user interface in which power and simplicity go hand in hand. Visit macmillanhighered.com/gardner12e for more information.

The Academic and Career Excellence System (ACES) is an instrument that measures student strengths in twelve critical areas and prompts students to reflect on their habits, behaviors, attitudes, and skills. Norm-referenced reports indicate whether students are at a high, moderate, or low skill level in particular areas. For more information go to macmillanhighered.com/ACES/catalog.

FOR MORE INFORMATION ON THIS BOOK OR ANY OF ITS SUPPLEMENTS

> Visit macmillanhighered.com/gardner12e

> Speak with your Macmillan sales rep

> View the chart on the inside front cover of the Instructor's Annotated Edition which shows you where to find each asset.

active learning strategies

The following exercises, which do not appear in the student edition, will help your students sharpen their critical skills for college success: writing, critical thinking, learning in groups, planning, reflecting, and taking action. Your students can also further explore the topics of each chapter by completing the exercises on this text's Web site at **macmillanhighered.com/collegesuccess/resources**.

1 WELCOME TO YOUR COLLEGE EXPERIENCE

WORKING TOGETHER The Many Reasons for College

Using the Your Turn: Make Good Choices, "The Choice to Become a College Student," as a prompt, have your students form small groups to discuss their reasons for attending college. In these groups, have students share the reasons that seem most relevant to them. Each group should compile a list of the most important reasons and share them with the class. Facilitate a discussion of similarities and differences in the lists. Also, discuss with your students which of these reasons they think have changed over time, and why.

EXERCISE 1.1 Solving a Problem

Ask your students to respond to the following questions in class or in an e-mail to you: What has been your biggest unresolved problem in college to date? What steps have you taken to solve it? Respond to students personally, and if they still have questions, invite them to meet with you during office hours.

EXERCISE 1.2 With or Without

This chapter stressed the differences between a high school education and a college education as far as earning power and other outcomes. Ask students to imagine they are still trying to decide whether or not to attend college. Drawing from the material in this chapter as well as from their own ideas, have students make a list of reasons to earn a college degree and a list of reasons not to go to college. For example, pipe fitters earn impressive salaries, while librarians earn much less. How do students justify a college education on those terms?

EXERCISE 1.3 Focusing on Your Concerns

Have students browse the table of contents of this book. Direct them to find one or more chapters that address their most important concerns. Make a list of the chapters your students have chosen, and note how many times students selected particular chapters. You will then be able to see the topics that concern them most and design your class to appeal to their interests.

EXERCISE 1.4 What Are Your Life Goals?

The following list includes some life goals that people set for themselves. This list can help students begin to think about the kinds of goals they might want to set. Ask students to put a check mark next to each of the goals they would like to achieve in their lives. Next, they should review the goals they have checked and circle the five they most want to achieve. Finally, students should review their list of five goals and rank them by priority on a 1-to-5 scale: 1 for most important, 5 for least important. Discuss the choices in class.

____ Supportive friendships

____ Good health

____ Financial security

____ A beautiful home

____ International fame

____ Work you are passionate about

____ A good love relationship

____ A satisfying religious faith

____ A meaningful life

____ Success in my profession

____ A personal contribution to social justice

____ A flexible schedule

____ A satisfying and fulfilling marriage

RETENTION EXERCISE SMART Goal Setting

Ask students to pick a goal—either short-term or long-term—and use the SMART template below to make their goal even more attainable. Students who are skilled at setting and attaining goals are more likely to persist in college.

Write a short-term or long-term personal goal that is related to your college experience. Use the SMART method to further develop your goal.

S: How can you make this goal more **S**pecific?

M: How will you **M**easure whether you have attained this goal at a high level?

A: How do you know that there is a reasonable chance you can **A**ttain this goal?

R: How is this goal **R**elevant to your interests and broader sense of life purpose?

T: What is your **T**ime period for achieving this goal?

For additional practice with the SMART method, refer to Chapter 1 (pages 16–17) which includes Figure 1.2, a blank SMART goal-setting guide for students to fill in with five goals. An example is provided to get them started.

2 TIME MANAGEMENT

WORKING TOGETHER Comparing Class Schedules

In small groups, have your students share their current class schedules. Encourage them to exchange ideas on how to handle time-management problems effectively and to point out the challenges they see in each other's schedules. Discuss ways that students can design more time-efficient schedules for the next term.

EXERCISE 2.1 Goal Setting

Have students complete the following lists:

A. List five goals you would like to set for yourself for the coming decade.
B. List two measurable objectives for achieving each of the goals you set.

EXERCISE 2.2 Your Daily Plan

Have students make a to-do list for the next day. Tell them to list all appointments and activities, noting the hours of the day. Have students label each item with an A, B, or C, with the A's deserving the most attention, and the C's deserving the least. Encourage students to check out the different calendar and personal planner formats, templates, and apps, many of which are available for free online or can be purchased at the campus bookstore.

RETENTION EXERCISE Tracking "Actual Time"

Some students will drop out of college because they are unable to manage their multiple time commitments. Help students become more aware of how they manage their time by using a weekly timetable (see example in Figure 2.2), a planner, or a calendar on their tablets or phones to keep track of how they spend time every hour for an entire week. Ask them to fill in every time slot. At the end of this week, ask students to count how many hours they spent on various activities. What activities merit more time? Which activities should take less time? In what ways did students waste time?

3 EMOTIONAL INTELLIGENCE

WORKING TOGETHER What Would You Have Done?

Share the following scenario with your students.

It's late afternoon on a Thursday, and the only thing between Josh and the weekend is a big biology test at 10:00 a.m. on Friday. There's a lot at stake with this test: It will count for one-third of his final grade. His cell phone rings. It's Susie with an invitation. "A group of us are planning to go out tonight. We thought about an early dinner and a movie. We won't be late," she says. The last time Josh went out on a night before a big test, he came home late. This time he is committed to coming home by 9:00 p.m. to review for the test. Josh goes out with Susie and her friends. He is having a wonderful time, and every time he thinks about going home, he says to himself, "Just a little longer and I will go." Before he knows it, it's 2:00 a.m., and the test is only eight hours away. Josh is exhausted and stressed. He has to decide whether he should sleep a few hours or pull an all-nighter to pass the test. He decides to sleep. He sets the alarm for 4:00 a.m., when he wakes up groggy and out of sorts. Josh starts to study, but his roommate's alarm goes off at 6:00 a.m. His roommate keeps hitting snooze, so the alarm goes off every 15 minutes. Josh is annoyed. He doesn't want to leave the room, but he has to concentrate. He complains, "I'm trying to study. Will you please be quiet!" His stress is getting worse, and now it's 8:30 a.m. His cell phone rings. It's Josh's mother reminding him about his grandmother's birthday. He snaps, "Mom, please don't bother me now. I am studying." He quickly hangs up; he has had it. This is his worst nightmare. He is stressed, on edge, and exhausted, and he feels a big headache coming on.

Divide the class into groups of four or five. Ask the groups to spend 15 or 20 minutes discussing the following questions: If you were in Josh's place, what would you have done? How would you evaluate Josh's emotional intelligence? What could he have done differently? What competencies does he need to improve? Then ask each group to report its responses to the entire class for discussion.

RETENTION EXERCISE Matching Behaviors with EI Competencies

Students who have difficulty managing stress and engage in self-destructive behaviors are often unable to complete a college degree. Have students match the unsuccessful student behaviors in the first column below with the related EI competencies in the second column that would help the student change or overcome the behavior. (Sometimes more than one competency relates to a single behavior.)

4 HOW YOU LEARN

WORKING TOGETHER Multiple Intelligences

After all students have completed the Multiple Intelligences Inventory, ask them to determine their highest point scores. Then, break the class into groups according to those scores. Ask group members to discuss the classes they're now taking and their intended majors. In discussion with the whole class, determine whether students with particular multiple intelligence scores are more likely to engage in certain activities, take certain classes, or select certain majors.

EXERCISE 4.1 Learning Styles Models

In small groups, ask students to discuss the four learning-style models that are presented in this chapter. Which was the easiest to understand? Which was the most difficult? Which of the models did group members like best? Why? Each group should report its opinions to the whole class.

FOR INSTRUCTORS ONLY

Unsuccessful Student Behavior	Related EI Competency
1. Experience stress and do not handle it well	A. Emotional self-awareness
2. Frequently feel overwhelmed	B. Self-regard
3. Don't get along with others	C. Assertiveness
4. Give up easily	D. Independence
5. Engage in destructive behaviors such as binge drinking and drugs	E. Self-actualization
6. Act very impulsively	F. Reality testing
7. Are not able to solve problems	G. Flexibility
8. Are dependent on others	H. Problem solving
9. Show unethical behavior such as stealing or cheating	I. Stress tolerance
10. Have trouble working in teams	J. Impulse control
11. Have very stereotypical views of others and are unaware of their biases and unwilling to change	K. Empathy
12. Are often sad	L. Social responsibility
13. Are not optimistic	M. Interpersonal relationships
14. Have an "I can't" attitude	
15. Blame others for their problems	
16. Think they will get a 4.0 GPA but have missed many classes	
17. Have a hard time making decisions without input from others	

EXERCISE 4.2 Using Your Five Senses to Learn

Have students refer to pages 64–77 in this chapter and decide which mode or modes of learning seem to work best for them: aural, visual, interactive, tactile, or kinesthetic. Ask for suggestions on how they can adapt to other styles. For example, if students are not aural learners, how can they use their preferred ways of learning to master information that is presented in lecture-style courses? Have students brainstorm ways to convert lecture material into a format that is a better match for how they best use their five senses in the learning process.

EXERCISE 4.3 Learning More about Learning Disabilities

Have students use the library or the Internet to find the names of three famous people not mentioned in this chapter who have learning disabilities and how they have dealt with or overcome those disabilities. Ask students to share with the class what they learned from their research.

RETENTION EXERCISE Multiple Intelligences and Success

After students take the short Multiple Intelligences Inventory, divide them into eight groups (one for each intelligence) and ask each group to think of ways that each intelligence (according to Howard Gardner) supports student success and the likelihood that someone will remain in college and graduate. Conversely, ask them to decide whether a specific intelligence makes it difficult for someone to be successful in college.

5 THINKING IN COLLEGE

WORKING TOGETHER Gathering Information for Decision Making

Divide the class into groups of four to six, and have each group choose a major problem on campus, such as binge drinking, cheating, college costs, parking, safety, and sexual assault. Between this class meeting and the next, students should seek information about their group's problem and identify possible solutions by interviewing a campus authority on the topic, searching campus library holdings, and/or conducting a survey of other students. During the next class, ask students to share their findings with other members of their group and cite their sources. Groups should try to reach a consensus on the best

way to solve the problem. If any members of the group are using emotional rather than logical arguments, point that out.

EXERCISE 5.1 Reflecting on Arguments

Review the lists of questions on pages 97–98 of this chapter with students. Are students asking themselves these kinds of questions when they read their textbooks and listen to or take part in discussions? Have students revisit the list each evening for the next week and think about whether they have asked such questions that day and tried to notice whether people were stating their assumptions or conclusions.

RETENTION EXERCISE Learning about a Liberal Education

Students who are enrolled in required general education or liberal arts courses often fail to see the relevance of those courses to their career or life plans. Such students might lose their motivation for academic work and decide to leave college. Discuss with students how a liberal college education is relevant because it teaches them to investigate all sides of an issue and all possible solutions to a problem before they reach a conclusion or decide on a plan of action. Make sure your students understand that the word liberal (from the Latin *libero*, meaning "to free") has no political connotation in this context, but represents the purpose of a college education: to liberate the mind from biases, superstitions, prejudices, and lack of knowledge so that students are in a better position to seek answers to difficult questions. Have students choose one of their instructors whose field is in the humanities (art, literature, languages, history, government, etc.), mathematics, or the sciences (social, biological, or physical). Students should make an appointment to interview the instructor about how a liberal education and the instructor's particular field of study contribute to a fuller life, no matter what a student's major might be.

6 READING TO LEARN

WORKING TOGETHER Thinking Back to High School

Ask students to write down the reading methods that worked best for them in high school. Then, ask them to share these methods with others in the class to initiate a discussion about how reading in college differs from reading in high school.

EXERCISE 6.1 Doing What It Takes to Understand

How far must students go to understand the material in a textbook? Here is one way to find out. Give them the following instructions:

1. Read a brief chapter in your textbook as if you were reading for pleasure.
2. Read it a second time, but pause at the end of each section to mentally review what you just read.
3. Read it a third time, pausing at the end of each section for review. Then go back and highlight important words or sentences.
4. Read it a fourth time, and do all of the above. This time, ask a friend to read with you, and discuss each passage in the chapter before going on to the next. Stop and take notes, write in the margins, and highlight.

Ask students to discuss how this process increased their understanding of the reading.

EXERCISE 6.2 Preparing to Read, Think, and Mark

Direct students to choose a reading assignment from one of their classes. After they preview the material as described earlier in this chapter, have students begin reading until they reach a major heading or have read at least a page or two. They should then stop and write down what they remember from the material. Next, have them go back to the same material and mark what they believe are the main ideas. Suggest that students list four main ideas from the reading so they don't fall into the trap of marking too much.

RETENTION EXERCISE Plan for Active Reading

Students who are poor readers will have great difficulty in college and, unless they improve their skills, are likely to drop out or flunk out. To help students improve their reading skills, ask them to bring a textbook from another course to your next class. During class, ask them to consider the four-step "Plan for Active Reading" on page 107. Ask them which step is the hardest and which is the easiest. The easiest may be "marking." Ask students to check their textbooks to see if any have too much highlighting or too many marks. The

hardest stage may be "reading with concentration." Ask students to get in small groups and develop a list of ideas for "concentrating while reading." Do any of the steps seem unnecessary to your students? Discuss the importance of each step.

7 GETTING THE MOST FROM CLASS

WORKING TOGETHER Comparing Notes

Present a small lecture to students on any topic of your choosing. The lecture can be related to the text or presented on another topic. Have students take notes on your lecture. Then ask students to pair up with others to explain their note-taking systems and share their notes. Ask them whether or not they agreed on what was important during the lecture. Give students your notes on the lecture so that they can compare and contrast their notes with yours. You might want to collect the students' notes and review them to make sure that they have taken notes on the most important points in the lecture.

EXERCISE 7.1 Encouraging Students to Speak Up in Class

Managing class participation is often a challenge for any first-year seminar instructor. Some students tend to monopolize group discussion while others seem reluctant to say anything. A way to help shy students feel more comfortable about speaking in front of the class is the "think, pair, share" technique. Pose an open-ended question to your students; give them a chance to think about how they would respond, and then ask them to discuss their response with one other person. Then, ask one or both students from each pair to share their response with the whole class. You may not have time to solicit a response from each pair of students. If time is limited, do this exercise over a few successive class periods on different topics to make sure that every student has a chance to speak for his or her pair.

EXERCISE 7.2 What System of Note Taking Works for You?

Have students pick one of their lecture courses and implement each of the methods of note taking described in this chapter over the next four or five class periods: Cornell, outline, paragraph, and list formats, or a combination. Ask students to decide which method seems to work best for them. Which method will be easiest to review when studying for tests?

EXERCISE 7.3 Using a Recall Column to Memorize

Have students refer to Figure 7.1 on page 138, and study the material provided in the right-hand column until they think they know it well enough to be tested on it. Cover the right-hand column and using the recall column, ask students to try to recite, in their own words, the main ideas from these sample notes. Allow them to uncover the right-hand column when they need to refer to it. Ask students whether this system seems to work. If not, why not?

RETENTION EXERCISE Engagement

Research finds that engagement can be linked to retention, particularly for students often considered at risk—first-generation students or historically underserved populations. Ask students working in small groups, either during class or out of class, to discuss the term *engagement* and what it means to them. Why do they think college and university educators focus so much on getting students engaged? Why do older students tend to be more engaged in learning than students just out of high school? Ask them to consider whether within their peer group it's cool to be "engaged in learning." Have groups share their ideas with the whole class.

8 STUDYING

WORKING TOGETHER The Name Game

Sitting in a circle, have students state their first names preceded by a descriptive adjective (for example, Sophisticated Susan, Tall Tom, and Jolly Jennifer). Proceed around the circle, having each student state his or her name and descriptor, followed by the names and descriptors of all preceding students. Students can help each other when someone's memory fails. After all students have had a turn, discuss what the class learned from the exercise.

EXERCISE 8.1 Getting the Big Picture

Select a concept from this book, and have students respond to the four questions under the heading "Improving Your Memory," listed on pages 159–60. Have students share their work in small groups. Then ask one person in the group to share with the entire class.

EXERCISE 8.2 Using Memory Strategies

Have students practice using association, visualization, and flash cards to improve their memories. Ask them to try the following strategies with a week's lessons from one of their courses:

1. Visualization. Close your eyes and "see" your notes or textbook assignments in action. Break your notes into chunks, and create a visual image for each chunk.
2. Association. Associate a chunk of information with something familiar. For example, if you want to remember that the word *always* usually signifies a wrong answer on multiple-choice or true/false quizzes, associate *always* with a concept such as "always wrong."
3. Flash cards. Write a key word or phrase from the material on one side of a card, and put the details on the other side. An example might be as follows: Write the words "Ways to Remember" on one side; on the other side, write, "Go over it again. Use all senses. Organize it. Mnemonics."

After students have tried all three methods, ask which method worked best for them.

EXERCISE 8.3 How Accurate Is Your Memory?

This exercise demonstrates how difficult it can be to remember things accurately. One student whispers the name of an object (e.g., lamp, bike, hamburger) to another student. The second student then whispers the word to a third student and adds a second word. The third student whispers both words to another student, adding still another word, and so forth. Each student who adds a word should write it down. When the final student recites the list, students whose words were left out or changed should speak up. The class should then discuss what strategies they were using to remember the list and why they forgot certain items.

RETENTION EXERCISE Creating an Acrostic

Memory is an essential study and test-taking skill that predicts success in college. To help students develop one memory strategy, divide the class into small groups, and have students select a list of words that someone in the group needs to remember. For instance, a group member might select the original thirteen colonies in the United States or famous composers of the Romantic period. Have each group create a sentence that everyone can remember, using the first letters of each word in the list. For instance, the composers Liszt, Chopin, Berlioz, Weber, Schumann, and Wagner could be remembered by using the sentence "Let's Call Brother While Sister Waits."

9 TEST TAKING

WORKING TOGETHER Forming a Study Group

Have students form a study group for a course. Students should think about their strengths and weaknesses in a learning or studying situation. Then have each study group brainstorm how each strength can help everyone in the group prepare for tests and exams. What helpful strengths will each student look for in another group member? How can their own strengths help others? Students should create a study plan for their study groups. They should review the test schedule for the course and set times for future meetings. What will each member of the group do in preparation for the next meeting?

EXERCISE 9.1 Designing an Exam Plan

Use the following guidelines to have students design an exam plan for one of their courses:

1. What type of exam will be used?
2. What material will be covered? Is the exam cumulative?
3. What types of questions will the exam contain?
4. How many questions do you think there will be?
5. What approach will you use to study for the exam?
6. How many study sessions—and how much time—will you need?

Now, ask students to list all material to be covered and create a study schedule for the week before the exam, allowing as many 1-hour blocks as they will need.

EXERCISE 9.2 Creating Your Own Peaceful Scene

To help students deal with test-taking anxiety, have them think about the most peaceful place they can imagine, real or imaginary. It might be a place they remember fondly from childhood, a special family vacation spot, a place where they always feel safe, a place they have always wanted to visit, or a place from a favorite book or movie. Now, have them think about what they would hear, see, smell, taste, and feel if they were there right now. Do not just have them think about how relaxed they would feel; ask them to be specific about what they would experience: the warmth of a fire, a gentle breeze, the sand between their toes, rain on the roof. Have students use all five senses to take themselves to their peaceful places. Practice this technique regularly with students, and they will be able to re-create peaceful scenes with ease when they need to relax.

RETENTION EXERCISE Test Taking

The connection between grades and retention is significant. As you approach the midterm, ask your students to think back on the tests they've taken so far. In small groups, ask them to identify their worst and best grades. Then, ask them to discuss with each other what factors might have affected their performance, especially factors they can control (such as amount and timing of preparation, sleep, exercise, diet, management of distractions, etc.).

10 INFORMATION LITERACY AND COMMUNICATION

WORKING TOGETHER Conducting a Group Search at the Library

Have students plan a library visit in groups of three. Before they go, one member of the group should call a librarian and ask for a brief meeting. When they arrive, they should ask the librarian to show them where to find reference books, periodicals, and scholarly journals. Students should also ask how to use online databases on the library computers to aid their searches. Decide which database each student will search, and have students search for a topic of their choosing. Students should print their findings and share them with the class. What did they learn?

WORKING TOGETHER Write, Pair, Write, Share

Direct your students to do this exercise in small groups of five or six. Use the following instructions:

1. Write. For about 10 minutes, use the freewriting technique to write about something that is on your mind. Remember, don't stop to think; just keep writing.

2. Pair. When you are told to stop writing, pair off with another student in your group, and share what you have written by talking about it. Listen to what the other person in your minigroup has to say about what you told her or him. Take notes if you wish.

3. Write. When you are next told to write, reflect on the interaction in your minigroup, but do it individually, on paper. How has the discussion reinforced, modified, or changed your original thoughts on the subject? Write this down.

4. Share. At the given signal, return to your small group of five or six. Appoint a leader, a recorder, and a reporter. Share your thoughts with the entire group. Listen to what group members have to say. Present your report to the group at large. Reflect on what learning has taken place and what the next steps should be. How might you apply this process to one of your other classes?

EXERCISE 10.1 Getting Oriented to Periodicals

To encourage students to get familiar with the periodicals in the library, have them complete the following tasks and answer these questions:

1. Find out how your library arranges periodicals (magazines, journals, newspapers). It probably isn't obvious, so don't hesitate to ask. Why do you think the periodicals are organized in this way?

2. Select an important event that was in the news the year you were born. To find out what was happening then, you might want to consult an almanac or ask a reference librarian to recommend a chronology. Find a contemporary (written at the time of the event) news report as well as a scholarly article that analyzes the event in a journal. Describe the event. Why was it significant? Note some of the differences you found between the news report and the scholarly article.

EXERCISE 10.2 Tempted to Take Shortcuts

Ask your students to read this scenario and identify all the ethical and practical problems with Jack's strategy. What suggestions would your students have for Jack?

At the end of history class on Monday, Jack's instructor told the students, "As you're finalizing the paper that is due on Friday, let me know if you have any questions about how to cite your sources. Remember to submit your paper at my office no later than 5:00 p.m." Jack panicked. He had completely forgotten about this paper and hadn't even begun working on it, much less thinking about how to cite sources. He raced out of class and went back to his room where his roommate was just waking up. Jack's roommate had the solution: "Just pick a topic that a lot of people have written about—something like World War II—go to Wikipedia, and copy all the information. Wikipedia even has all the sources listed." Jack had never used Wikipedia before, but he thought "borrowing" the Wikipedia write-up was a good last-minute solution.

EXERCISE 10.3 Using the Guidelines for Successful Speaking

An important objective of first-year seminars is to help students become more comfortable in giving oral presentations. Student presentations in first-year seminars are usually brief and can be focused on an assigned topic or a topic chosen by the students themselves. Be sure to direct your students to the Guidelines for Successful Speaking in this chapter before they give their presentations. Let them know that they will be evaluated (either formally or informally) on the degree to which they have followed these guidelines.

EXERCISE 10.4 Getting Comfortable in Your Library

To encourage students to get familiar with the library, have them complete the following activity:

Unobtrusively observe what goes on around the information services or reference area (not the circulation desk where you check out books). Watch at least five transactions. Watch the people who ask questions, and watch the staff people who answer them. Does it appear to you that the "customers" receive friendly, competent help? Do the staff members sit and point, or are they on their feet? Do they sometimes accompany inquirers to stack areas or work with them at the computer stations? How might what you observe influence your strategy for getting help if and when you need it?

RETENTION EXERCISE Getting Involved

Students who are involved on campus will be more likely to persist with their college careers. This exercise links involvement with strategies to increase learning and skill building.

Make a list of offices, centers, or activities on your campus in which students can become involved and can practice their writing and speaking skills. (Examples could include the campus radio station, a newspaper or literary magazine, student government or other leadership activity, a Greek organization, a tutoring center, a writing center, etc.) Divide students into pairs or small teams of three or four and have each group visit one of these offices to learn more about its focus and requirements for student involvement. Have each group make a brief presentation to the class about what group members learned, and especially what writing or speaking experience students could gain by becoming involved with these activities.

11 RELATIONSHIPS

WORKING TOGETHER Roommate Gripes

Residence hall staff report that the most common areas of conflict between housemates or roommates are those listed below. Have students check the ones that are true for them.

_____ One roommate needs quiet to study; the other needs music or sound.

_____ One roommate is neat; the other is messy.

_____ One roommate smokes; the other hates smoking.

_____ One roommate brings in a lot of guests; the other finds them obnoxious.

_____ One roommate likes the room warm; the other likes it cool.

_____ One roommate considers the room a place to have fun; the other considers it a place to study.

_____ One roommate likes to borrow; the other isn't comfortable lending.

_____ One roommate is a morning person; the other is a night owl.

_____ One roommate follows all the residence hall rules; the other breaks them.

Ask students who select the same conflicts to work in a small group to create ideas for resolving these differences.

EXERCISE 11.1 Looking for Love

Have students read the profiles (Facebook, Instagram, Twitter, or others) of fellow students. Ask them to respond to the following questions in

writing: What questions, issues, or themes do people seem to be writing about most? What does this tell you about people's needs in relationships? In class, discuss what students discovered.

RETENTION EXERCISE Interviewing an Instructor

Assign students to select one of their course instructors and schedule an interview. Encourage students to work in pairs or teams. Provide guidelines for students, such as the following:

- How to schedule an interview appointment
- The importance of being on time for the interview
- Appropriate questions to ask, such as how and when the instructor developed an interest in teaching, where the instructor went to undergraduate and graduate school, and what the instructor likes most or least about teaching

Ask students to give a short (5–10 minute) oral presentation in class or write a short report about their interviews. Send a brief e-mail or written "thank you" to instructors whom your students interviewed. Let them know that you designed this assignment to help your first-year students learn more about instructors and become more comfortable with them out of class.

12 DIVERSITY

WORKING TOGETHER Reflecting on Identity

1. Have students form groups of four to six people. Have them identify areas in which they all share similarities, and keep a written record of those areas. Group members must all agree with an item before it can be added to the list. Next, ask students to create a list of differences.
2. Have students respond to the following questions: How easy or difficult was it to come up with similarities and to agree on them? To what level of depth do the group similarities go? (For example, "We all have hair" versus "We are all religious people.") Was it easy or hard to identify differences? Which list was longer?

EXERCISE 12.1 Examining the Curriculum

At this point, students might have identified some majors that interest them. Have students use your campus's course catalog to identify courses in majors that focus on the topics of multiculturalism and diversity. Why do they think academic departments have included these subjects in the curriculum? How would studying diversity and multiculturalism help students to prepare for their fields of choice?

EXERCISE 12.2 Appreciating Your Gender

Have students read the following four questions pertaining to gender and create a list of answers:

1. What aspects do you like about being your gender?
2. What are the best things that have happened to you because you are that gender?
3. What are some things that have happened because of your gender that you do not want to experience again?
4. What would you like other people to know about your gender?

RETENTION EXERCISE Diversity

Students who feel marginalized at your institution because of their race, gender, sexual orientation, economic status, or other characteristics will be at risk for dropout. Ask your students to take the perspective of someone different from them, and write a short essay on whether the institutional environment is or is not supportive of that individual. Examples would be white men or women, students of color, students of different religions, students with different sexual orientations, students of different ages.

13 WELLNESS

WORKING TOGETHER Recommendations for Stress Management

If your students could make only three recommendations to an incoming first-year college student about managing college stress, what would they be? Have students use their experience as well as what they have learned in this chapter to make recommendations. In groups of four, have students compare their lists with those of other students and try to come to a consensus on the three most important recommendations.

EXERCISE 13.1 Monitoring Your Stress

Following is a list of physical and emotional conditions that people can feel when stressed. Have students check those that best describe them.

Then, have students review those they have checked and write a paragraph describing how they could manage the symptoms of stress using the techniques suggested in this chapter.

_____ My breathing is rapid and shallow.

_____ I have trouble solving problems.

_____ I feel tightness in my chest.

_____ I feel irritable.

_____ I feel jittery.

_____ I have trouble concentrating.

_____ My pulse races.

_____ My muscles feel tense, especially around my shoulders, chest, forehead, and back of neck.

_____ My hands are cold or sweaty.

_____ I have butterflies in my stomach.

_____ I experience diarrhea or constipation.

_____ I have to urinate more frequently.

_____ My mouth is dry.

_____ I tremble or feel shaky.

_____ I have a quaver in my voice.

_____ Things easily confuse me.

_____ I have trouble remembering things.

_____ I feel overwhelmed.

_____ I am anxious about things I have to do.

_____ I feel depressed.

_____ I feel frustrated.

_____ I have insomnia.

_____ I wake up far too early and can't go back to sleep.

_____ I have noticed changes in my eating habits.

_____ I feel fatigued a good bit of the time.

EXERCISE 13.2 Doing a Weekly Check

Have students keep a food, physical activity, and sleep journal for three days. The goal is to write down everything they eat and drink, as well as the amount of sleep and physical activity they get each day. After the three days, have students evaluate their food journals.

- Did they have an even distribution among the categories?
- Have they met the recommendation of five fruits and/or vegetables per day?
- Did their grains consist of complex carbohydrates, such as whole wheat?
- Did their liquids consist of high-calorie choices, such as soda and beer?

Have students review their physical activity journal at the end of the three days.

- Did they get 30 minutes of physical activity most days? Did they stretch after exercising?
- Did they work all the major muscle groups during their activity?

Have students analyze their sleep during the period.

- Did they get the recommended seven to nine hours of sleep per night?
- Did they follow the tips listed in this chapter regarding sleep?
- Did they notice a pattern between the amount of sleep they got in a given night and how well they ate?
- Were they as physically active on days when they did not get a good night's sleep?

At the end of the week, have students write about their experiences.

- Did they feel better or worse during this experiment?
- What will they do about their diet, sleep, and physical activity once this experiment is over?

EXERCISE 13.3 What's Your Decision?

Although students might know about the strategies to keep themselves from contracting an STI, knowledge doesn't always translate into behavior. Ask students to brainstorm a list of all the reasons they can think of why people wouldn't practice the prevention strategies of abstinence, monogamy, or condom use. Then, go back over the list and ask students to consider whether each reason would apply to themselves (yes, no, or maybe). In this way, students can better evaluate where they stand on the issue of safer sex and determine what areas they might need to work on to ensure that they protect themselves—always!

RETENTION EXERCISE Finding a Balance

Students who persist in college are more likely to be those who take a balanced approach to their lives as college students. Ask students to list all the components of their college experience—for instance, studying, going to classes, taking tests, living in a residence hall, relating to family, working on or off campus, hanging out with friends, exercising, playing a sport—and to rate each as "increases my stress level" or "reduces my stress level." Ask students whether they are in balance—that is, whether they are

engaged in as many stress-reducing activities as stress-increasing activities. Make a list of those activities that create the most stress for students, and discuss stress-reducing techniques in class.

14 MONEY

WORKING TOGETHER Financial Advice

Divide the class into groups of four or five, and have each group appoint a discussion note-taker. Ask members in each group to share any financial advice they have received from friends or family. Bring the class together, and ask each note-taker to report on what group members shared. Ask students to comment on the kinds of advice they're receiving and the overall challenges of money management.

EXERCISE 14.1 Calculating Interest Charges

Ask students to select a recent credit card bill and note on a piece of paper the amount spent that month. Then have them assume they charged the same amount in each of the next eleven months and paid only the minimum payment each month. Now have them calculate the balance they will have in one year, including interest charges. To help them complete this assignment, refer them to online interest rate calculators, such as the one at bankrate.com/brm/calc/minpayment.asp. If they're not sure of some amounts, have them use 15.99 percent as their APR and 31.99 percent as the APR default rate.

EXERCISE 14.2 Debit or Credit?

By a show of hands, ask how many students have at least one credit card. Then ask how many have debit cards. Ask students who have at least one of each which they use the most and why. Ask students who have credit cards but no debit card to explain why they don't feel they need the latter. Underscore the difference between debit cards and credit cards.

RETENTION EXERCISE Being Financially True to Yourself

Assign a paper asking students to share any concerns they have about their current financial situation. Have them include any improvements they have made in keeping track of their money, as well as any areas they feel are getting out of hand.

After reading the papers, share the positives and negatives with the class without identifying student contributors.

15 MAJORS AND CAREERS

WORKING TOGETHER Work-Shadowing

Have students do this exercise with a partner: At the career center, arrange to "work-shadow" a professional in a field that interests you. Spend at least a day observing this person. Reflect on what you observe. Did the work environment meet your expectations? Are you more or less interested in this occupation? You and your partner should then share your conclusions with the rest of the class.

EXERCISE 15.1 Finding Your Interests

1. Have students complete an interest inventory at the campus career center or online. One such inventory is the Holland Self-Directed Search, at **self-directed-search.com** (there is a fee of around $9.95 for the results). Or they can visit the Princeton Review and take the Career Quiz (**princetonreview.com/careers -after-college.aspx**). Students should list their top five occupational interests based on this instrument.

2. Have students interview a professional in one of these fields. Encourage them to conduct the interviews in teams. In the interviews, students should find out as much as they can about the education that is required, skills they would need to be successful, typical career opportunities, and the outlook for the future. Have them identify five key things that they learned from the interviews.

EXERCISE 15.2 Using Your Career Library

Have students visit the campus career center's library. Many of these libraries have materials organized by the Holland model that you can ask students to use in Exercise 15.1. This method of organization enables students to research careers that are compatible with their personality types. Suggest that they talk to a career counselor about some of the jobs that interest them. Have students summarize in writing what they have learned.

EXERCISE 15.3 Writing a Résumé and Cover Letter

Give students this assignment:

1. Prepare two résumés, using the chronological model for one and the skills model for the other. Then, using either model, write another résumé that projects what you would like your résumé to contain five years from now. This University of Utah Web site provides examples of ways to write and organize chronological and skills résumés: **usu.edu/career/students /resumes.php**.

2. Using the career center or campus library, find a professional person whose career path matches your major or career interests. Write this person a cover letter to go with your résumé, and turn these in to your instructor.

RETENTION EXERCISE My Current Thinking about Career Choice

Students who are clear about their career direction are more likely to persist and graduate from college. Ask students to make a list of their personal interests, preferences, characteristics, strengths, and skills. They should match the list to the skills and interests needed by successful people in a field that interests them and note other influences that might be drawing them to their career (such as their parents' preferences). Have students share their notes with a career counselor to get some feedback on how well their career interests mesh with their strength and skills.